This book is the property of:

. . . .

College/School . . . .

Technology of Skilled Processes

Basic Engineering Competences

Power Transmission

Editorial Panel

N A Butterworth, MSc, CGIA, CEng, FIMechE, FIProdE

G H Farnworth, MScTech, PhD, CEng, MIMechE, MIProdE

V Green, TEng(CEI), MBIM
Head of Department of Engineering Crafts
Huddersfield Technical College

C Sutcliffe, OBE, MSc, CEng, MIMechE
Vocational Curriculum Services
City and Guilds of London Institute

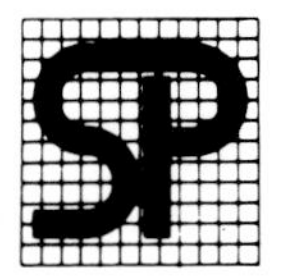

Published as a co-operative venture between

Stam Press Ltd

and

City and Guilds of London Institute

Syllabus

Technology of Skilled Processes 367-1

Section	Process
1	Observing Safe Practices
2	Moving Loads
3	Measurement and Dimensional Control (1)
4	Marking Out
5	Work and Toolholding
6	Removing Material
7	Forming
8	Joining
9	Fabrication
10	Soft Soldering, Hard Soldering and Brazing
11	Fusion Welding
12	Power Transmission
13	Assembling and Dismantling
14	Interpreting Drawings, Specifications and Data

Syllabus

Basic Engineering Competences 201

Basic Engineering Technology
201-1-01

01 Industrial Studies
02 Observing Safe Practices
03 Moving Loads
04 Measurement and Dimensional Control (1)
05 Marking Out
06 Work and Toolholding
07 Removing Material
08 Joining
09 Interpreting Drawings, Specifications and Data
010 Assembling and Dismantling

Basic Fabrication and Welding Technology
201-1-07

01 Forming
02 Fabrication
03 Soft Soldering, Hard Soldering and Brazing
04 Fusion Welding

Basic Maintenance Technology
201-1-09

01 Forming
02 Soft Soldering, Hard Soldering and Brazing
03 Power Transmission
04 Measurement and Testing of Electro-Mechanical Systems (1)

Science Background to Technology
201-1-04

01 Basic Physical Quantities, Electricity and Magnetism
02 Forces
03 Pressure
04 The Principles of Tool Construction; Materials Technology

SUPPORTING BOOKS

Book titles	Covering	Covering
Basic Engineering	**Syllabus** 367-1	Syllabus 201-1-01
Observing Safe Practices and Moving Loads	Section 1 and 2	02-03
Measuring and Marking Out	Section 3 and 4	04-05
Workholding and Toolholding, Removing Material	Section 5 and 6	06-07
Joining	Section 8	08
Interpreting Drawings, Specifications and Data	Section 14	09
Assembling and Dismantling	Section 13	10
Fabrication and Welding		Syllabus 201-1-07
Forming	Section 7	01
Fabrication	Section 9	02
Soft Soldering, Hard Soldering and Brazing	Section 10	03
Fusion Welding	Section 11	04
Maintenance		Syllabus 201-1-09
Forming	Section 7	01
Soft Soldering, Hard Soldering and Brazing	Section 10	02
Power Transmission	Section 12	03
Science		Syllabus 201-1-04
Basic Physical Quantities, Electricity and Magnetism		01
Forces		02
Pressure		03
Principles of Tool Constructions; Material Technology		04

201 – Basic Engineering Competences
201-1-09 Maintenance Engineering

The contents of this book have been designed to cover the requirements of the City and Guilds Basic Process Competence Syllabus (367-1), section 12. The contents of the component 03 of the City & Guilds Basic Engineering Technology Syllabus 201-1-09 are identical and thus equally covered by this book.

As listed, the heading references in this book conform with those in the syllabus section 12 scheme 367-1. In the 201 scheme syllabus items are numbered sequentially and prefixed with the component number, e.g. item 1 in syllabus 03 is 3.1.
Below, in brackets following the page numbers, we give the 201 syllabus sequence numbers.

Contents Power Transmission

PART 1 **03**

PART 2 **questions** **03**

Introduction

This book is intended for those who are, or will be, doing a practical job in industry.
It is specially written for those who need their technology as a background to their work and as a means of adapting to changes in working practices caused by technological advance. Where words such as "he" or "craftsman" appear in this series, they are to be interpreted as "he/she", "craftsman/woman".
This new series of textbooks presents the technology in terms of competence rather than working from a conventional theoretical base, i.e. the material will help readers understand:
- the use of
- the change to
- the development of
- other uses of

industrial process technology and skills.

This book has been compiled after a survey of the industrial skilled processes which form the nucleus of occupational schemes and pre-vocational courses of the City and Guilds of London Institute and a comparison with provisions elsewhere in Europe.

Three basic facts emerged:
- the technology is common to many different schemes though the contexts of applications are very different;
- the technology is being taught in a variety of workshops in a variety of exercises related to the immediate needs of students and their industries; these industrially-related exercises formed excellent learning tasks and provided clear motivation for students because of their immediate relevance;
- the technology is so well integrated with the 'first-task need' that students did not recognise its relevance to many other tasks they would be called upon to perform.

This book seeks to build on the learning tasks and to provide a means of learning and generalising the technology, so that the immediate job is better understood and better done, new tasks using the same process technology are more quickly mastered and updating or retraining is easier and more effective.
The editors would welcome further constructive suggestions which should be addressed to:
Stam Press Ltd
Old Station Drive
Leckhampton Road
Cheltenham GL 53 ODN

Australia AEP, Blackburn (Melbourne)
België Plantyn, Deurne (Antwerpen)
Belgique Plantyn, Bruxelles
BRD Stam, Köln
France Casteilla/Educalivre, Paris
Great Britain Stam Press, Cheltenham
Stanley Thornes, Cheltenham
Nederland Educaboek, Culemborg
Educa Int., Culemborg
De Ruiter, Gorinchem
Suisse Delta & Spes, Denges (Lausanne)

First published in Great Britain 1987
as a co-operative venture between Stam Press Ltd and the City and Guilds of London Institute

Reprinted 1991

ISBN 0 85973 0271

Printed in Great Britain by Martin's of Berwick.

Project Structure and Use of Syllabus Bank and Supporting Books

1 The TECHNOLOGY associated with a given industrial process is a common requirement, but the APPLICATIONS vary by occupation and task, so a distinction has to be made between:

(a) THE AIM of the process: eg. to bend, metals, to drill, etc.

(b) THE LEARNING and ASSESSMENT: related to the application(s) specific to the industry to which the candidate belongs or aspires, or to the context of scheme chosen as a basis of study.

2 The approach suggested for the learning and assessment of any process technology is as follows:

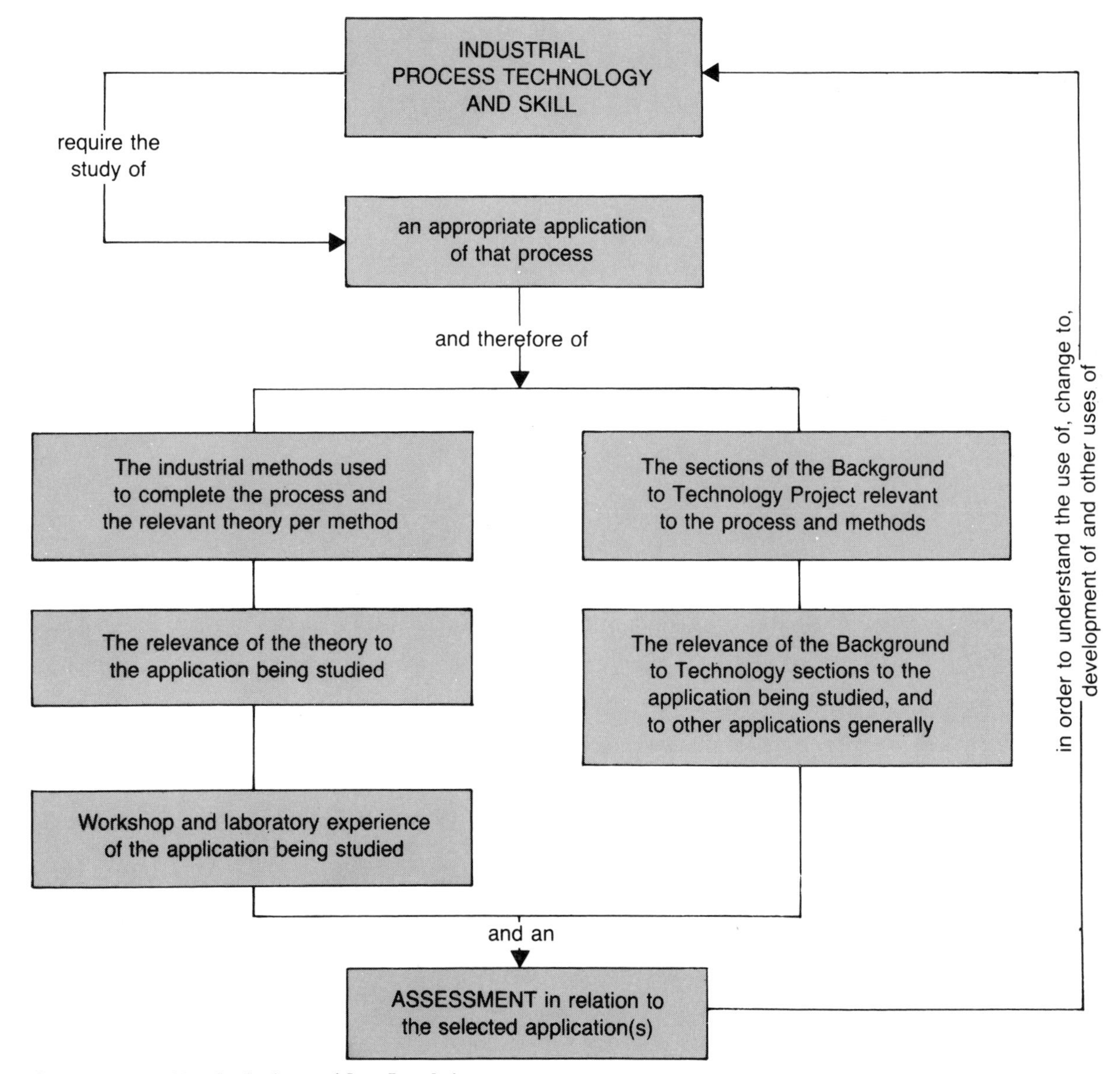

1 Transmission mechanisms

Foreword

A mechanism can be defined as a system of mutually adapted parts working together. The concept of a transmission mechanism is illustrated below:

- *A vice* – a tool used to clamp a workpiece tightly. The screw and nut together form a mechanism. This mechanism allows a rotary motion to be converted into a rectilinear (straight line) motion.
- *A drilling machine* – provision is made to transmit the rotational movement of the electric motor to the spindle; a drilling machine is, therefore, a transmission mechanism.
- *A camshaft* – which operates a valve by means of a push rod, is also a mechanism. The combination of camshaft, push rod and rocker enables a valve to be lifted at a pre-determined moment and for a pre-determined distance.
- The assembly of components used to direct a satellite in a calculated orbit round the earth is another example of a mechanism.
- The assembly of components which, for mass production purposes, trace a pattern and by that means direct a number of cutting torches or blades to cut several plates simultaneously, is also a mechanism.

The book deals only with the mechanisms which are used in tools, machines and engines. They are referred to here as 'transmission systems'.

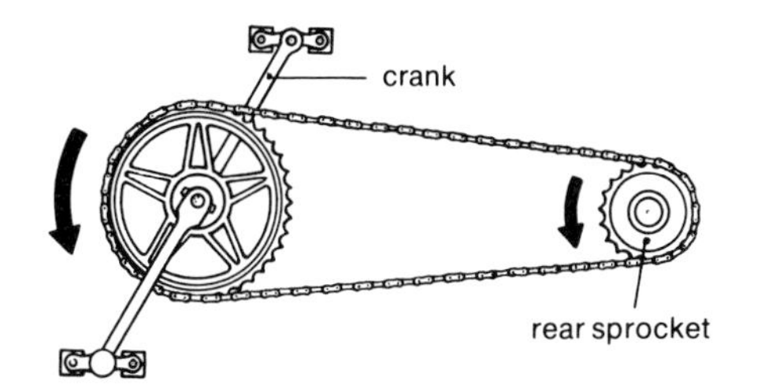

1.1 Chain transmission of a bicycle

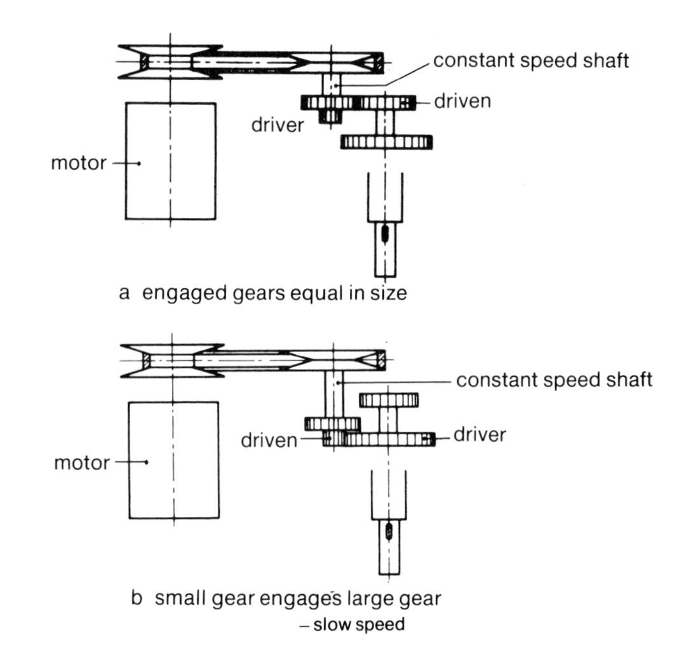

1.2 Transmission mechanism of a drilling machine – diagrammatic

1.a Purpose of mechanisms

Mechanisms are used to:

- *establish a connection between two shafts.* The chain connection between the pedal crank and the driving sprocket on the rear wheel of a bicycle is shown in Fig. **1**.1
- *change the speed of a shaft.* The principle of using gears to change the speed of rotation of a shaft driven by a constant speed shaft is illustrated in Fig. **1**.2
- *reverse the direction of rotation of a shaft.* Examine Fig. **1**.3a; gear 1 is rotating in a constant direction and is transmitting motion to gear 4 via gear 2. If the gears 2 and 3 are moved to the position illustrated in Fig. **1**.3b the drive to gear 4 is via gear 3 and gear 2 with the result that the rotation of gear 4 is reversed.

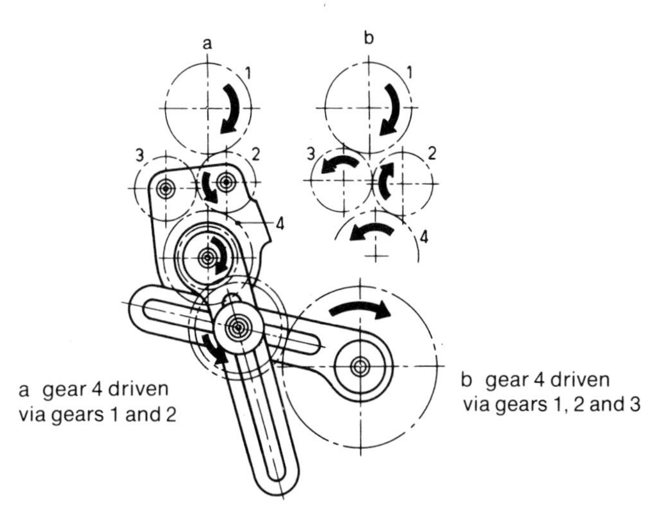

1.3 Reversing mechanism

- *convert one kind of motion to another.* A power hacksaw is shown in Fig. **1.**4. The rotary motion of the drive is converted to the reciprocating motion of the blade by the linkage.

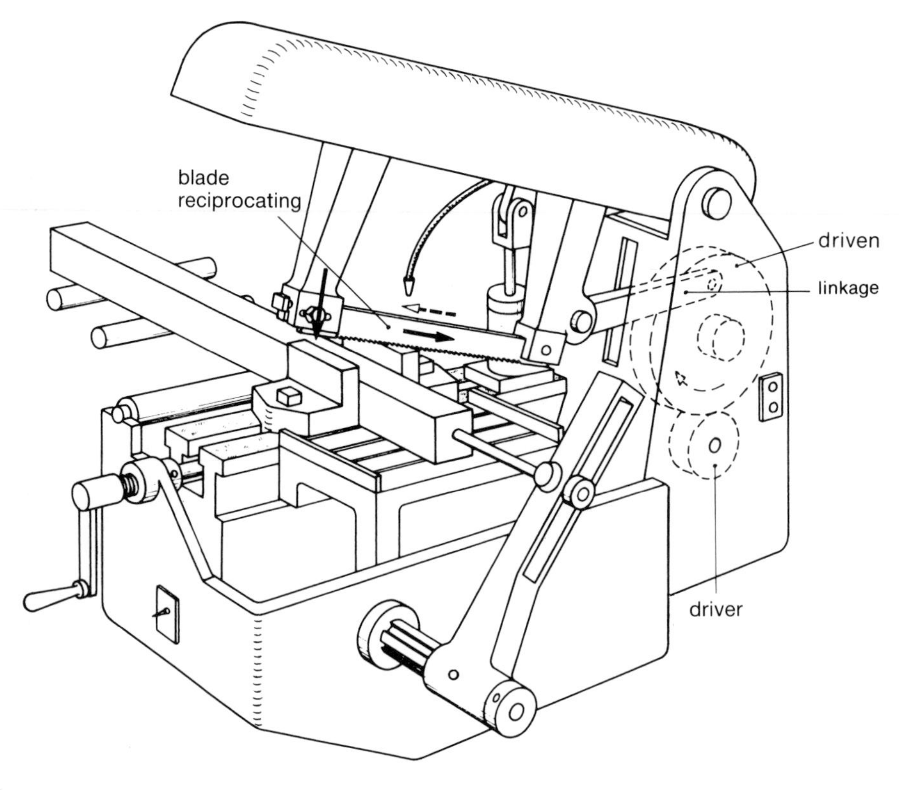

1.4 Power hacksaw

1.b Terminology of mechanisms

Table 1.1 Explanation of terms

Term	Explanation
Motion	A body is said to be in motion when it is changing place or position relative to its surroundings.
Distance	This is a measure of the length of travel made by a point on the body in motion. The SI (Système International) unit of length is the *metre*, symbol m. Derived units are the kilometre (km = 1000 m) the centimetre (cm $= \frac{m}{100}$), the millimetre (mm $= \frac{m}{1000}$).
Force	That which causes motion or a change in motion is called a force. The SI unit of force is the *newton*, symbol N. A derived unit is the kilonewton (kN = 1000 N). Forces are sometimes designated kgf (kilogram force). 1 N $\simeq$ 0.1 kgf or 1 kgf $\simeq$ 10 N.
Time	The unit of time is the *second* symbol s. Other units of time are the minute (min = 60 s) and the hour (h = 3600 s).
Torque	Torque is defined as 'the turning moment exerted by a tangential force acting at a distance from the axis of rotation'. Torque is measured as the product of the force and the distance. The unit of force is the *newton metre*, symbol Nm.
Linear velocity (speed)	Velocity is the distance travelled per unit of time. The SI unit of velocity is the *metre per second*, symbol m/s. Derived units are the centimetre per second (cm/s) and the kilometre per hour (km/h).
Rotational velocity	The unit of rotational velocity is the *revolutions per minute*, symbol rev/min. Consider a point on the rim of a wheel. If the wheel rotates, the 'speed' of rotation is a measure of the number of times in a minute that the point goes through the full 360° turn.
Acceleration	Acceleration is defined as 'the rate of change in velocity, expressed in metres per second squared. The SI unit of acceleration is the *metre per second per second* (m/s^2).
Deceleration	Deceleration is negative acceleration. It is the rate of slowing down and is expressed as $-$m/s^2.
Peripheral velocity	This is the velocity of a point on the periphery of a rotating body. It is expressed in *metres per second* (m/s), as is linear velocity.
Work	Work done is the force multiplied by the distance travelled in the direction of the force. The SI unit of work is the *newton metre* (Nm) or *joule* (J) i.e. when a force of 1 newton advances its point of application by 1 metre the work done is said to be 1 joule.
Power	Power is the work done per unit of time. The SI unit of power is the *newton metre per second* (Nm/s), or the *watt* (W). A derived unit is the *kilowatt* (kW). 1 kW = 1000 W. **Note.** The unit of work, *horsepower* is still used; it is not an SI unit: 1 hp = 746 W, 1 kW = 1.34 hp
Efficiency	Efficiency is expressed in terms of a ratio: $\frac{\textit{work output}}{\textit{work input}}$ *or* $\frac{\textit{power output}}{\textit{power input}}$
Friction	Friction is a force opposing the sliding or rolling of one body over another. There are two forms of friction: • *Friction at rest.* This is the opposing force when a body is brought into motion. • *Friction in motion.* This occurs when a body moves at constant velocity.
Slipping	Slipping occurs in some degree between any two components where one is driving the other. The obvious example is the slipping that takes place between a pulley and a belt. However, slipping also takes place between gears as the clearance between the driving faces is taken up.

1.c Types of motion

2.c.i Path or trajectory

When we consider the shape of the trajectory a distinction can be made between:

- *Arbitrary motion:* Consider the apparently aimless flight of the fly (Fig.**1.**5a). There appear to be no set patterns (or rules) governing the movement or the speed at which it is carried out. This is called arbitrary motion.
- *Rectilinear motion:* Movement in a straight line at a constant speed is termed rectilinear motion (Fig. **1.**5b).
- *Circular motion:* Movement in a circle in a constant plane (Fig. **2.**5c) is termed circular motion.
- *Helical motion:* Circular motion in a changing plane is termed helical motion (Fig. **1.**5d).

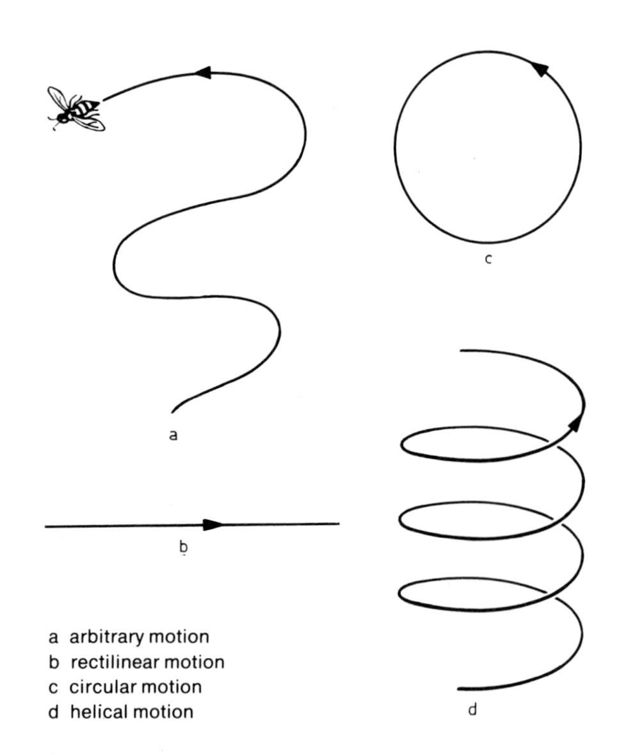

a arbitrary motion
b rectilinear motion
c circular motion
d helical motion

1.5 Types of motion

1.c.ii Velocity

The variation in motion caused by velocity is best illustrated graphically. Fig. **1.**6 shows a series of curves with velocity plotted against time.

- *Random motion* (Fig. **1.**6a): The velocity changes constantly.
- *Uniform motion* (Fig. **1.**6b): The velocity remains constant.
- *Uniformly accelerated motion* (Fig. **1.**6c): The velocity increases uniformly.
- *Uniformly decelerated motion* (Fig. **1.**6d): The velocity decreases uniformly.

1.c.iii Form or progress

The variation caused by the form of the motion can be:

- *Continuous motion:* The graphical illustrations in Figs. **1.**6a, b, c and d all show continuous motion.
- *Intermittent motion* (Fig. **1.**6e): Here the motion is continually stopping and starting.

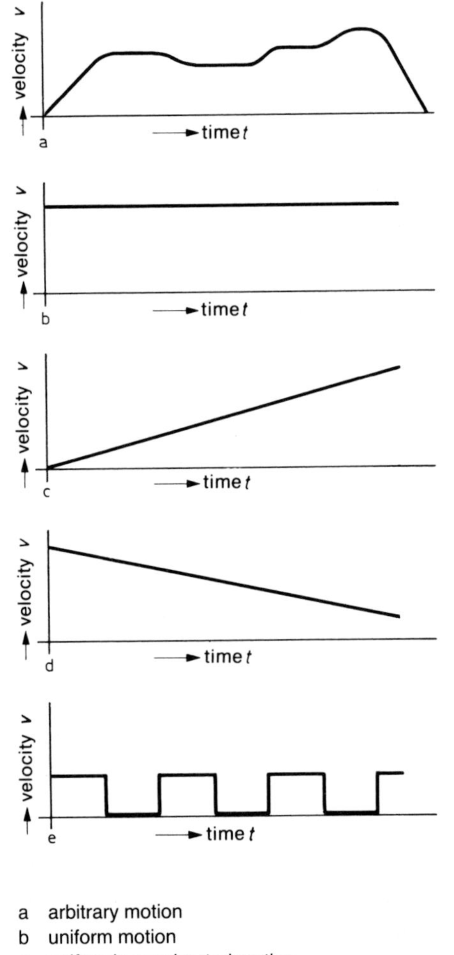

a arbitrary motion
b uniform motion
c uniformly accelerated motion
d uniformly decelerated motion
e intermittent motion

1.6 Graphical illustration of motion with time

1.d Methods of achieving motion

Motion may be achieved in several ways. These methods are listed below:

1.d.i Mechanical power transmission mechanisms

Motion is achieved when a power source is able to transmit the generated power via some form of mechanism in order to carry out work.

- *Chain:* pressure applied to the crank of a bicycle is transferred by the chain to the rear sprocket of the bicycle, causing the wheel to rotate and the bicycle to move (Fig. **1.**1).

- *Belt:* power from an electric motor is transferred via the drive belt to the drill spindle (Fig. **1.**7).
- *Gear:* probably the most common mechanism used to achieve motion is the gear train. As the tension on a watch spring is released in a controlled manner by the escapement, the released energy is transmitted through a gear train to drive the hands. The power from the engine of a car is transmitted via the gearbox and transmission assembly to the driving wheels. A simple gear system is shown in Fig. **1.**8.

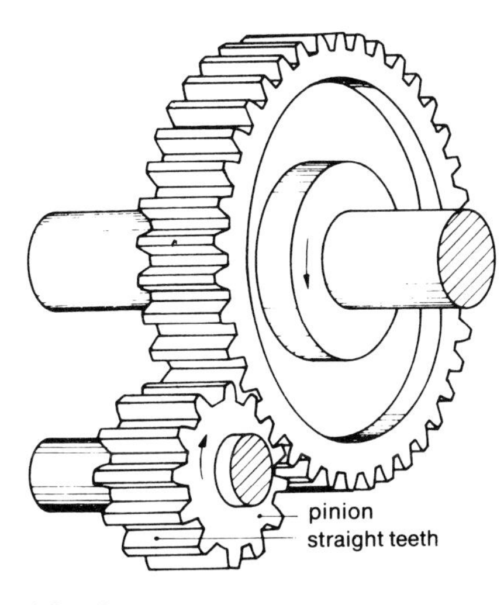

1.8 Gears

1.d.ii Power sources

There are several methods of providing the power to achieve motion:

- *Muscle power:* This is the oldest means of providing power. Human or animal power has been used for centuries to move loads.
- *Water power:* The energy available when a head of water is released is probably the oldest mechanical method of achieving motion. A flow of water is used to turn a water wheel, which in turn operates the machinery in a flour mill.
- *Wind power:* The energy of the wind can be harnessed by windmills and used for drainage purposes or milling. A recent development is the use of wind to generate electricity.
- *Internal combustion engine:* The energy released by the burning mixture in the cylinder forces the piston down the cylinder. This linear motion is converted via a crank to the rotary motion of a shaft (Fig. **1.**9).
- *Steam power:* This can be used in two ways
  a. The expansion of water vapour when subjected to heat is used to move a piston in a cylinder, in much the same way as in the internal combustion engine.
  b. The release of super-heated steam under great pressure on to the blades of a turbine produces a rotary motion, e.g. a large electrical generator.

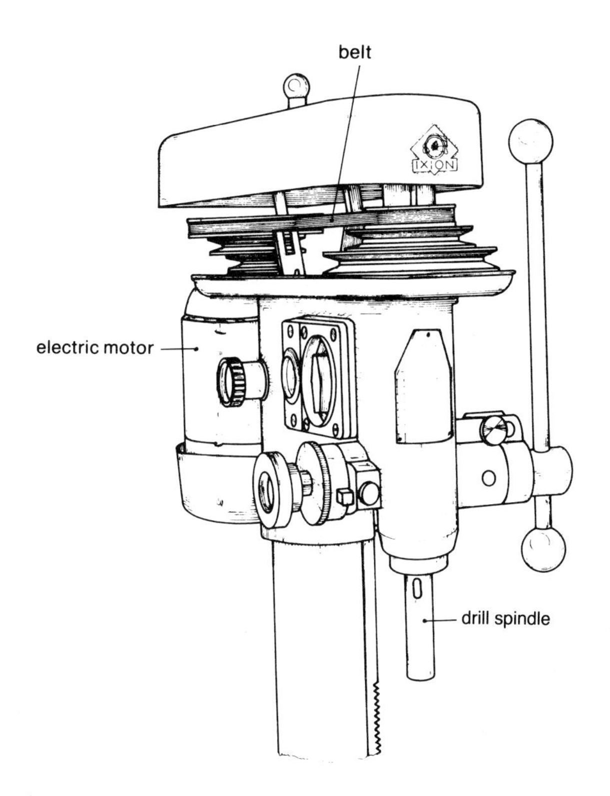

1.7 Drilling machine

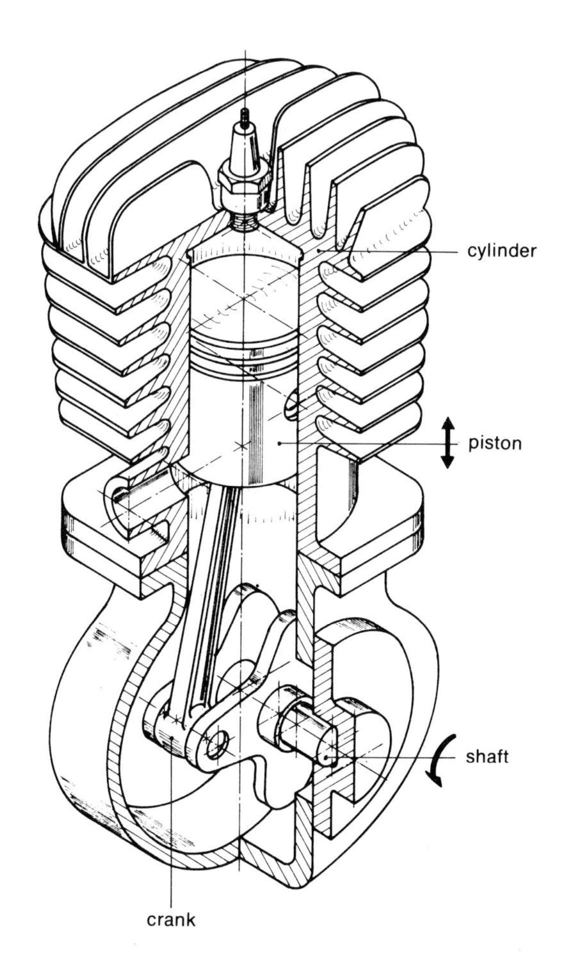

1.9 Single-cylinder petrol engine (Moped)

- *Hydraulic power:* A liquid cannot be compressed to any great degree. This fact is used in hydraulic engineering. Consider Fig. **1.**10. If the handle is pumped, fluid is drawn from the reservoir, through the non-return valve and into the cylinder. Since a liquid cannot be compressed, the cylinder piston is forced to move to make way for the increased amount of liquid in the cylinder. If a load is placed on the piston the load will be moved.
- *Pneumatic power:* Air under pressure can be used to operate valves, to move a piston in a cylinder or to activate pressure switches. Fig. **1.**11 shows a hopper being used to load material into a lorry. The jaws of the hopper are operated pneumatically.
- *Electrical power:* An electric motor powers a shaft from which many mechanisms can be activated. (Fig. **1.**12).
- *Combination of all the above:* Many mechanisms have a combination of power sources, e.g., the compressor of a pneumatic power system is likely to be electrically powered.

1.11 Pneumatically-operated sandchute

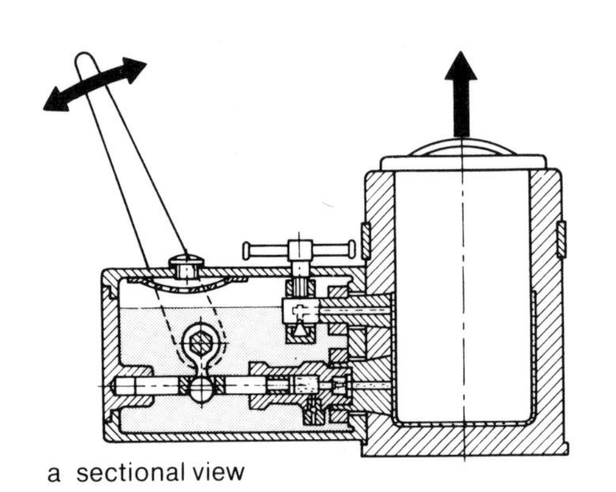

a sectional view

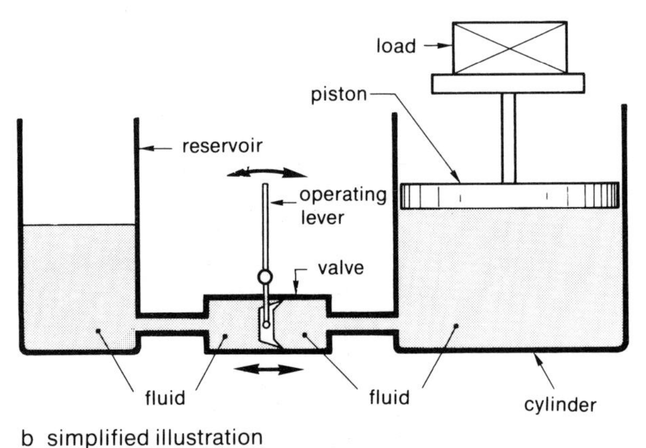

b simplified illustration

1.10 Hydraulic jack

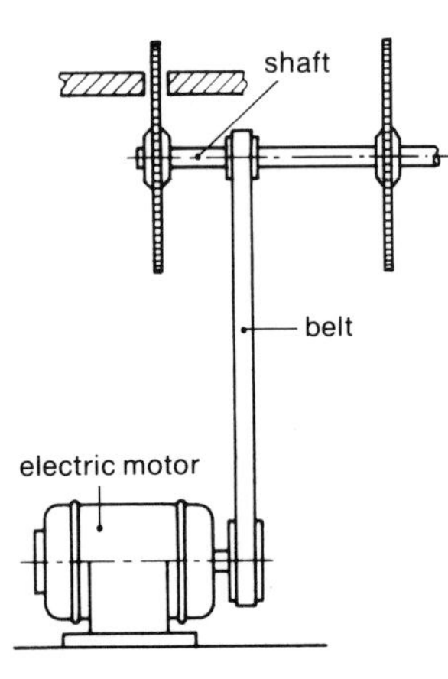

1.12 Electric motor driving a shaft

2 Applications

According to their application mechanisms can be sub-divided as follows:

a *Control mechanisms* – These include on, off, reversing and speed control switching devices (Figs. **2.**1 and **2.**2). The oil container being transported on the moving belt (Fig. **2.**1) will trip the control valve (Fig. **2.**2), causing the steering valve to operate in order that the container is shunted from the main belt into a collecting spur.

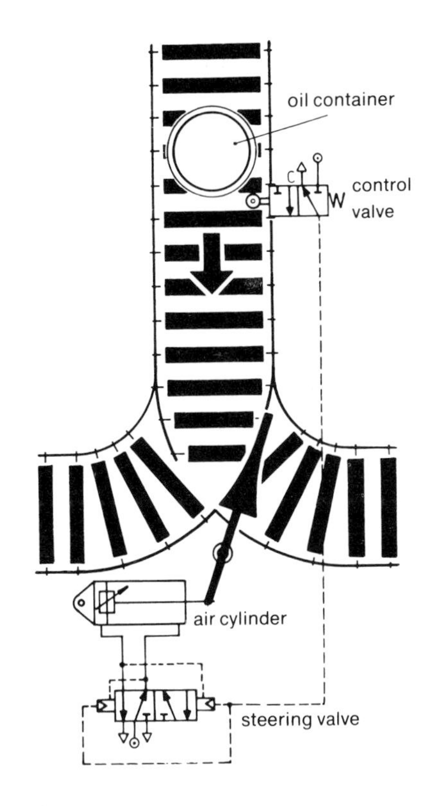

2.1 Pneumatically-operated switch

2.2 Control valve

b *Drive mechanisms* – These include belts, pulleys and shafts. These are used for powering machine tools (Fig. **2.**3).

Note. A machine tool is defined as 'any power-driven, non-portable machine designed primarily for shaping and sizing metal parts', e.g. lathes, milling machines, planing machines.

2.3 Drive mechanism

c *Reversing mechanisms* – These are used for reversing the direction of rotation (Fig. **2.**4).

Consider Fig. **2.**4. The driving shaft passes through, but is not keyed with gears F and C and rotates in a constant direction. The sliding dog clutch is keyed to the driving shaft and can be moved by the reversing handle to engage with either gear G or gear F. If gear F is engaged the drive to the main shaft is via gears F, C, B and A. If, however, gear G is engaged the drive to the main shaft is via gears G, D, F, C, B and A. By the introduction of gear D the rotation of gear C and hence the main shaft has been reversed.

d *Feed mechanisms* – These are used in machine tools to carry cutting tools for material removal (in lathes) as on-off switches and as feed regulators (Fig. **2.**5).

e *Conversion mechanisms* – These convert a rectilinear motion into a circular motion or vice versa (Fig. **2.**6).

f *Locking and interlocking mechanisms* – These are applied
- to prevent a drive from being engaged while a protection cage surrounding a machine is open.
- to prevent the drives of two mechanisms, which act in opposite directions, from being engaged simultaneously.

g *Coupling mechanisms* – These engage and disengage aligned shafts (Fig. **2.**7).

The main purpose of all the mechanisms mentioned, with the exception of the locking mechanisms, is to transmit motion. Therefore these mechanisms may be classified as transmission mechanisms.

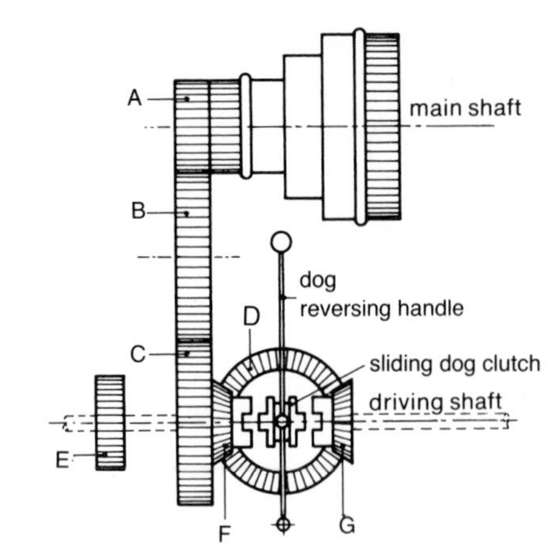

2.4 Reversing mechanism

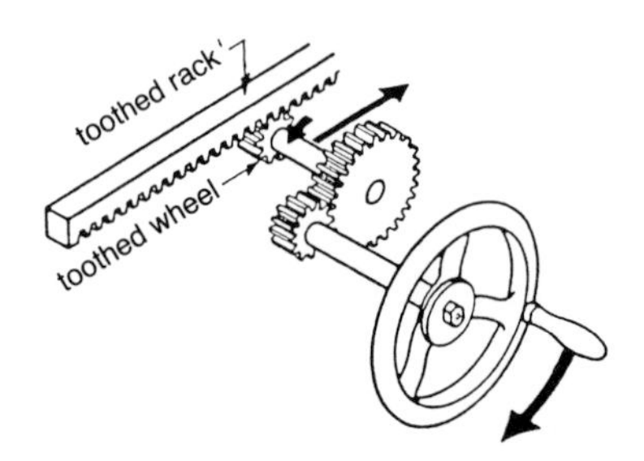

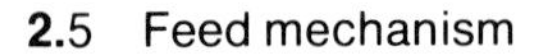
2.5 Feed mechanism

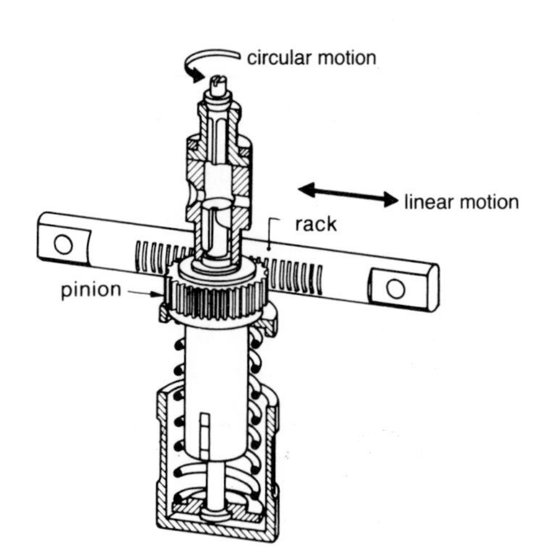

2.6 Conversion mechanism - rack and pinion

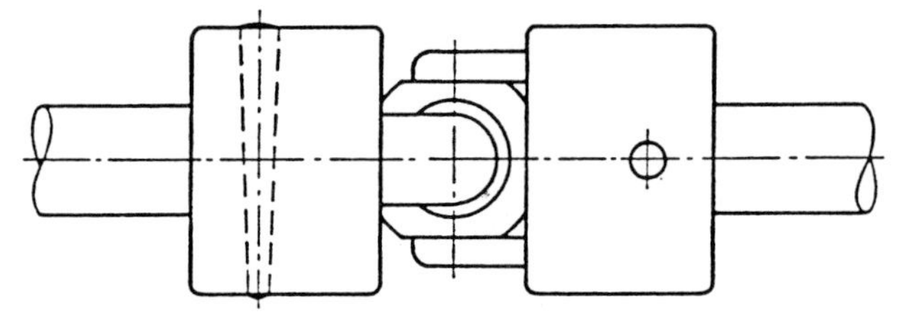

2.7 Coupling mechanism

3 Operating principles of transmission systems

3.a Mechanical transmission systems

Transmission is established in the following manner:

3.a.i Friction drives

- between a flat belt and a pulley (Fig. **3**.1)
- between a vee-belt and a vee-pulley (Fig. **3**.2)
- between flat or cone-shaped friction wheels (Fig. **3**.3)
- between conical surfaces (Fig. **3**.4).

Friction transmissions will always slip. Vee-belts will slip less than flat belts.

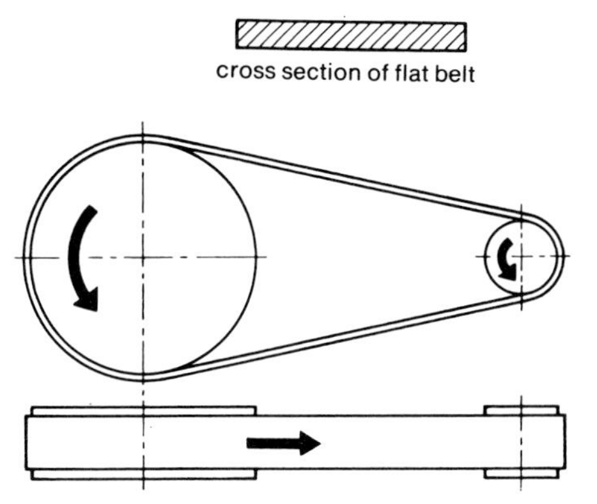

3.1 Flat belt drive

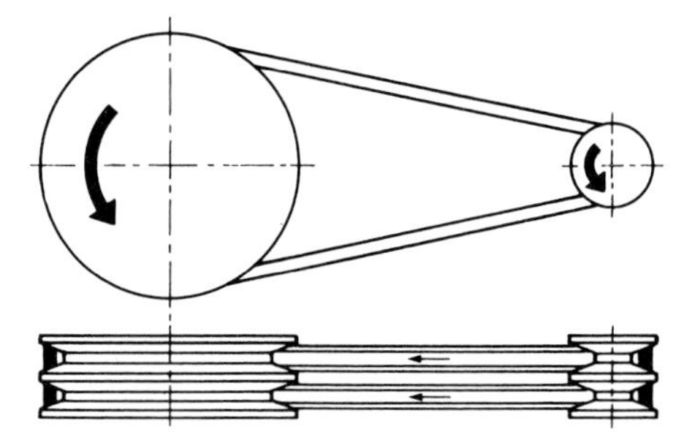

3.2 Vee-belt drive

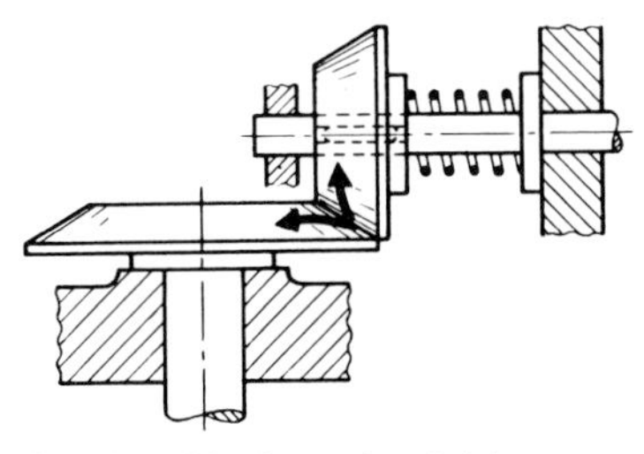

3.3 Conical friction wheel drive

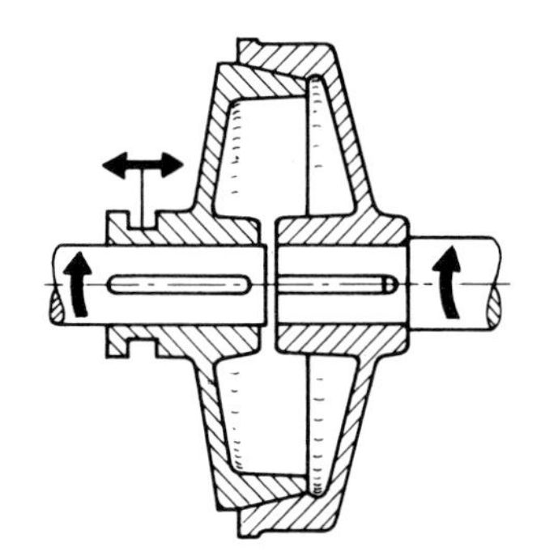

3.4 Cone surfaces

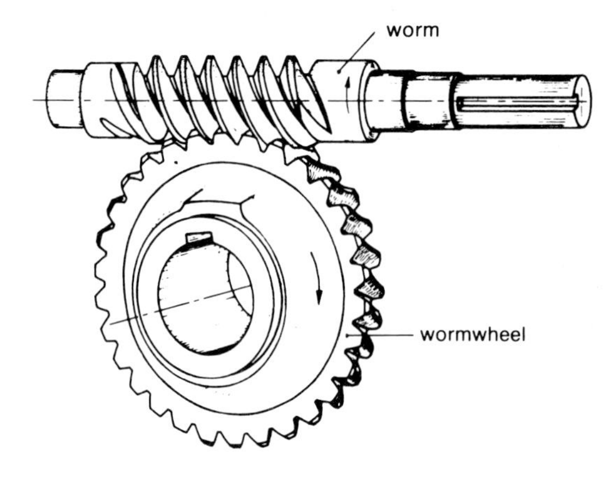

3.5 Worm and wormwheel

3.a.ii Engagement

- gear teeth (Fig. **1**.8)
- a worm and wormwheel (a form of gear) (Fig. **3**.5 and **3**.6).

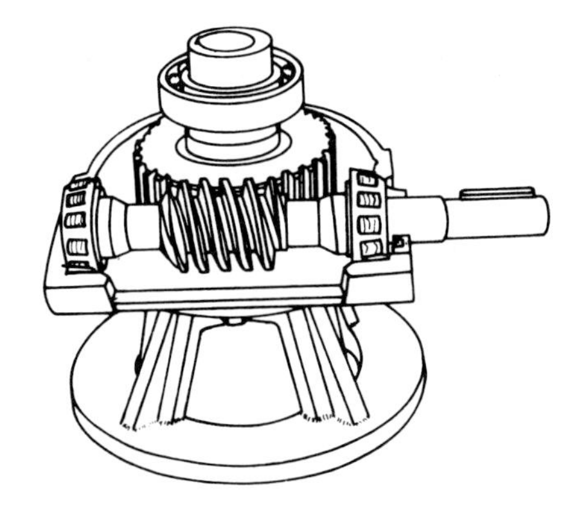

3.6 Gearcase

- a rack and pinion (Fig. **3.**7)
- a chain and sprocket (Fig. **3.**8)
- serrated belts and pulleys (Fig. **3.**9)
- a screw and nut (Fig. **3.**10).

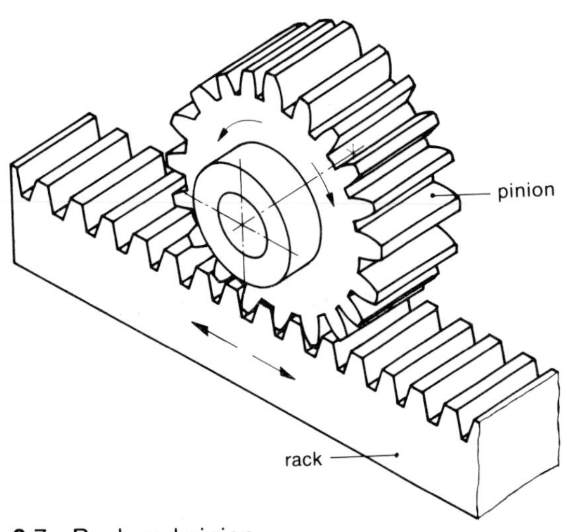

3.7 Rack and pinion

3.8 Chain and gear transmission with sprocket

3.9 Serrated belt transmission

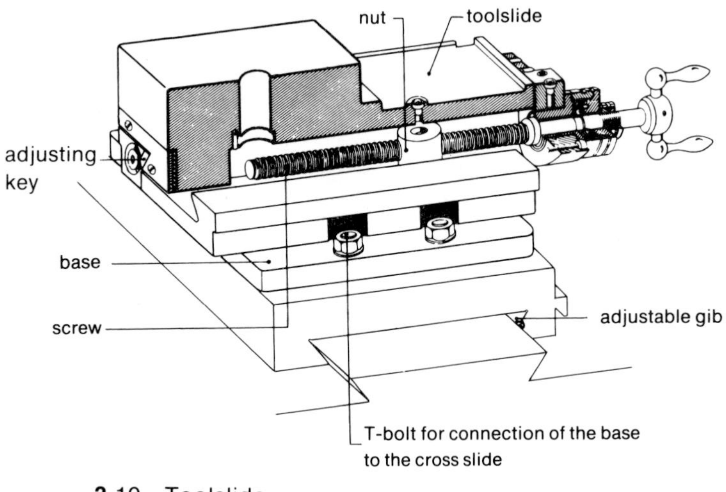

3.10 Toolslide

3.a.iii Derived from circular motion

Various types of motion may be derived from circular motion. The course of the derived motion depends on the manner in which guidance is provided. This is explained schematically in Figs. **3.**11, 12 and 13 where the distance travelled by point P depends on the diameter of the circle described by point K.

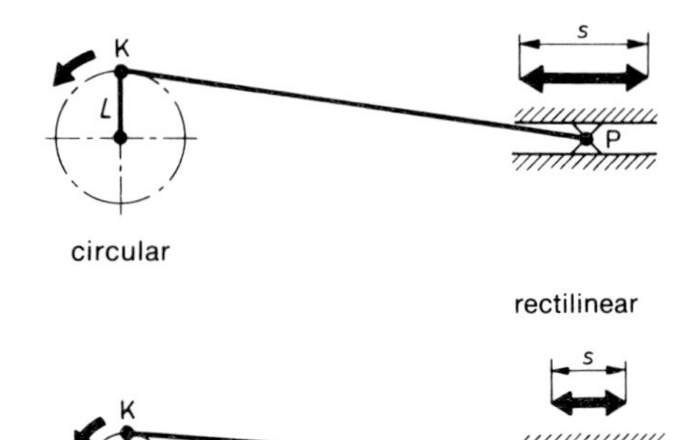

3.11 Crank-connection rod mechanism

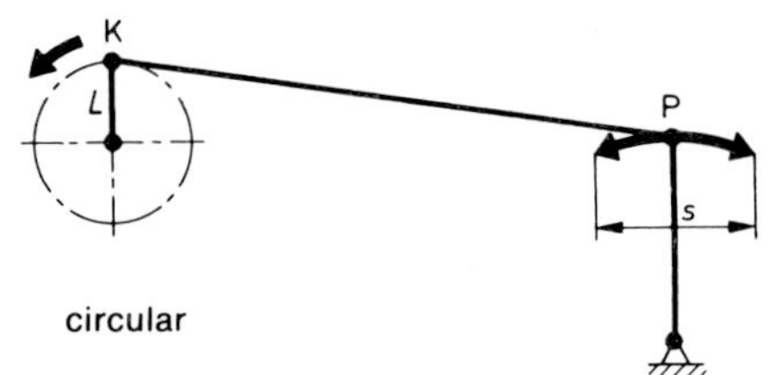

3.12 Oscillating motion

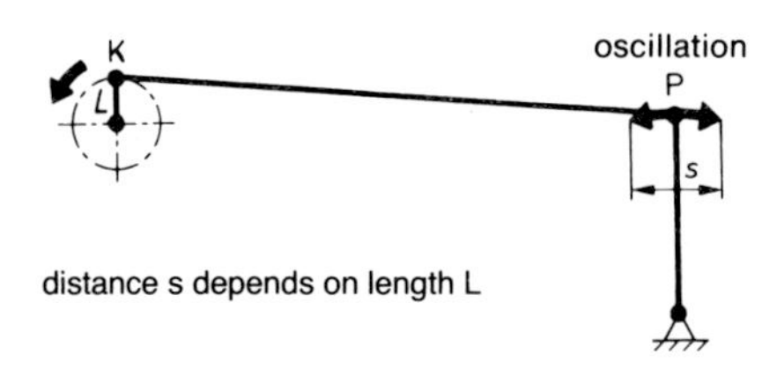

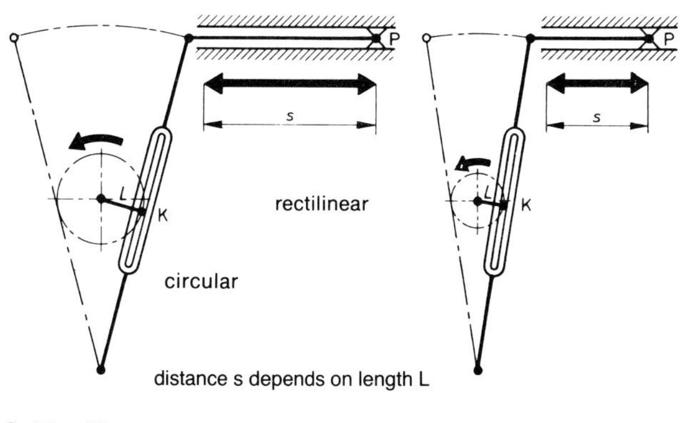

3.13 Shaper linkage

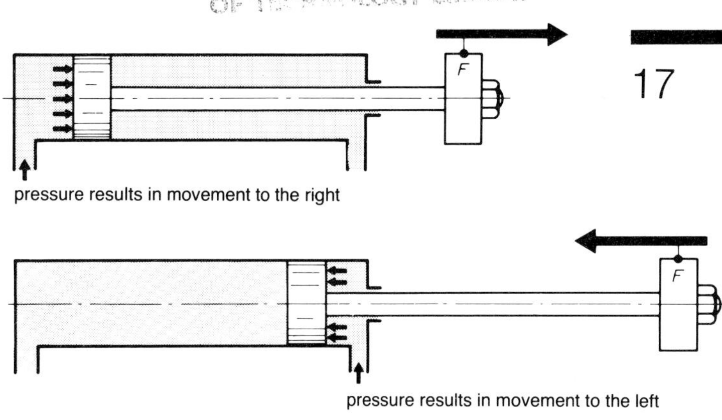

3.15 Double-acting hydraulic cylinder

3.b Hydraulic and pneumatic systems

3.b.i Hydraulic operation

The operation of hydraulic mechanisms is based on the principle of uniform pressure transmission in a fluid. Fluid pressure is utilised to:

- exert a great force (Fig. **3.**14). The pressure applied on the small surface area at F_1 is transferred to the large area at F_2. The resultant force F_2 is much larger than the applied force F_1.
- obtain a smooth reciprocating movement (Fig. **3.**15).

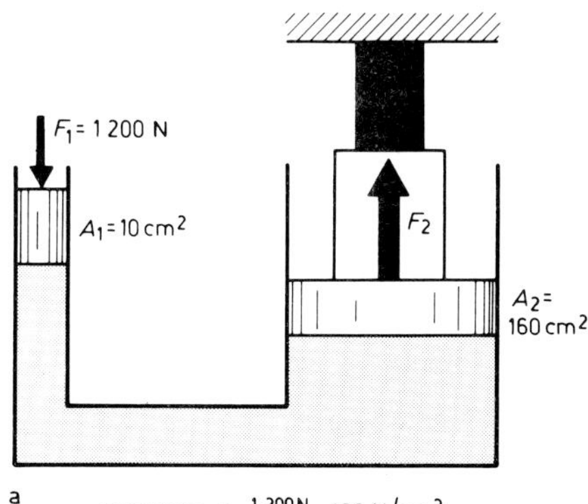

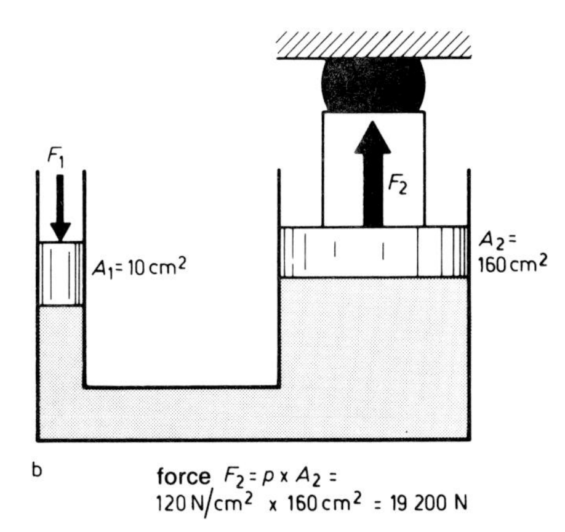

3.14 Principle of hydraulic press

3.b.ii Pneumatic operation

The action of pneumatically operated mechanisms is based on the uniform transmission of pressure in a gas (air). An example is the air-operated brakes on earlier large vehicles. Air stored at pressure is released when the brake pedal is depressed, to act on a piston which forces the brake shoes into contact with the brake drum.

3.c Transmission ratio

The transmission ratio is a velocity relationship and can be stated to be the relationship between the speed of the driving shaft or gear to the speed of the driven shaft or gear.
Mechanisms to transmit circular movements are subdivided into:

3.c.i Transmission with fixed ratios

Speed variation of transmission by vee-belts (Fig. **3.**16), gears (Fig. **3.**17) or by vee-belts and gears (Fig. **3.**18) is achieved only in pre-determined steps.

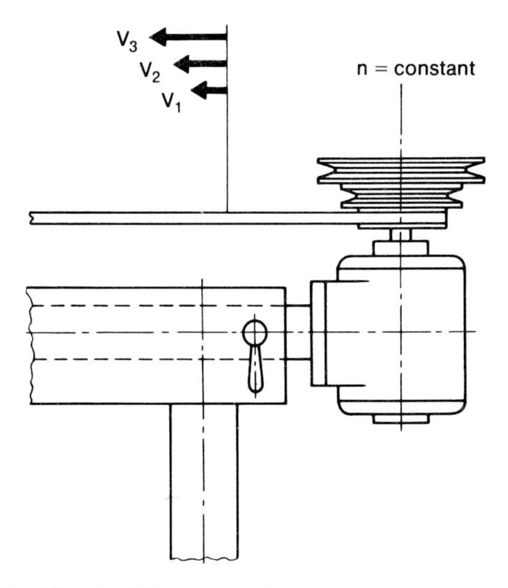

3.16 Vee-belt transmission

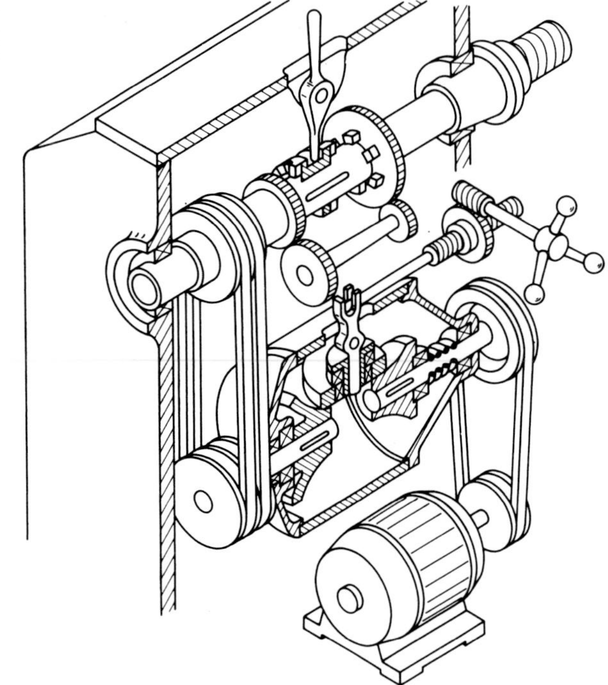

3.18 Combined vee-belt and gear transmission

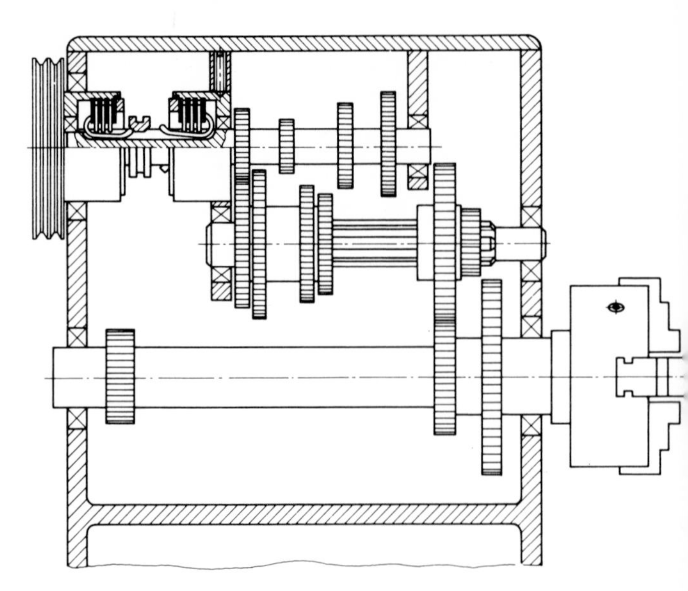

3.17 Gear transmission

3.c.ii Transmission with adjustable ratios

The friction transmission shown in Figs. **3.**19 and **3.**20 and the speed variator of Fig. **3.**21 may be adjusted for any speed between highest and lowest defined limits. Speed variation may also be achieved by a variable speed prime mover, which might be powered by electricity, petrol, diesel oil or steam.

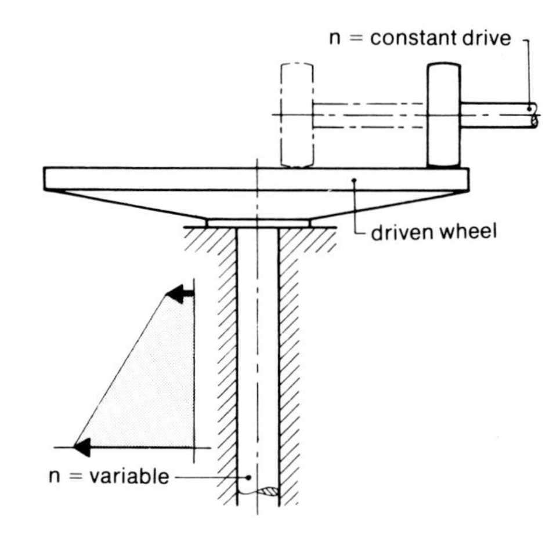

3.19 Friction transmission

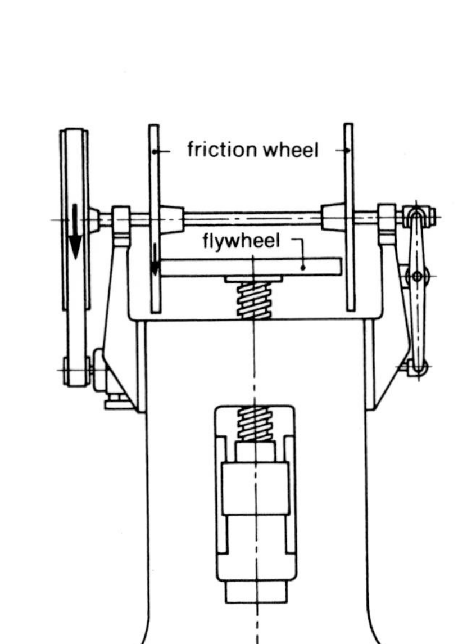

3.20 Friction transmission

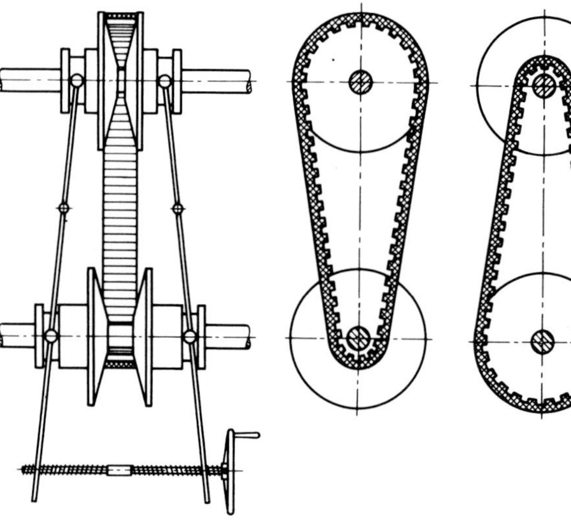
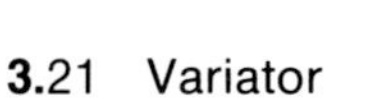

3.21 Variator

4 Shaft position

4.a Classification of shaft positioning

From the relative positions of the shafts of a transmission mechanism, we can distinguish between:

i aligned shafts (Fig. **4.**1)
ii shafts at a slight angle (Fig. **4.**2)
iii parallel shafts (Fig. **4.**3)
iv crossed shafts (Fig. **4.**4)
v intersecting shafts (Fig. **4.**5).

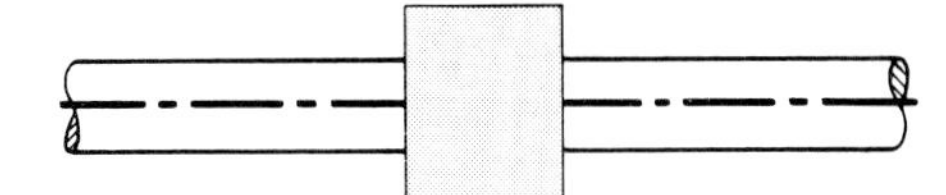

4.1 Aligned shafts

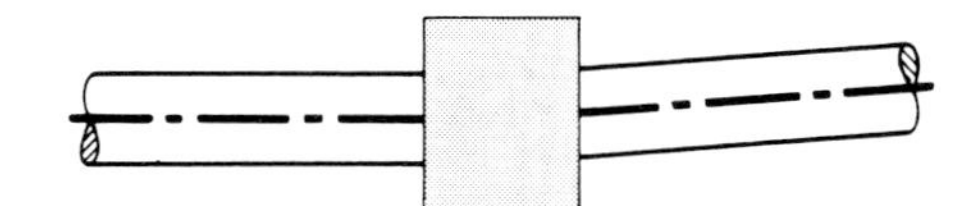

4.2 Shafts at an angle (up to 4°)

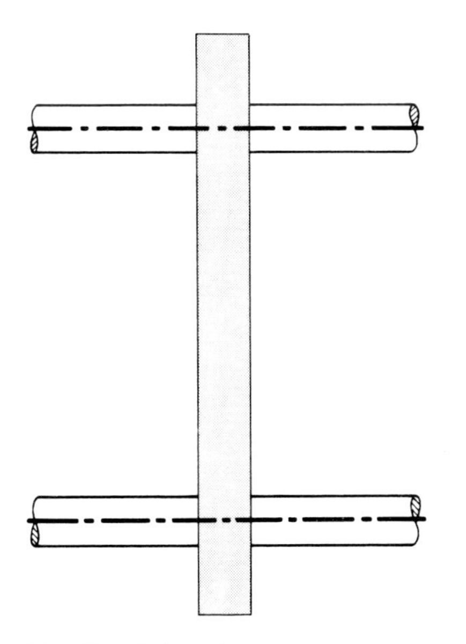

4.3 Parallel shafts

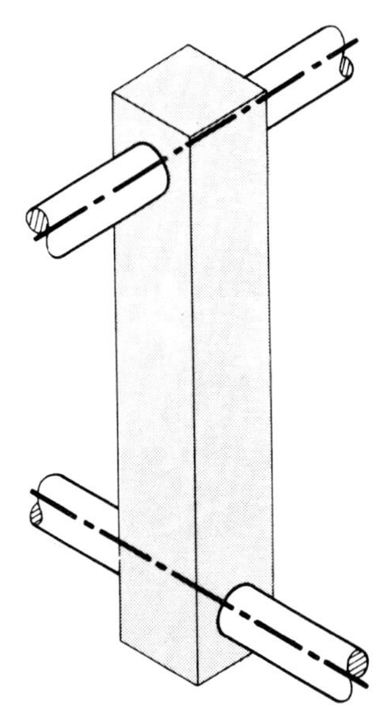

4.4 Crossed shafts

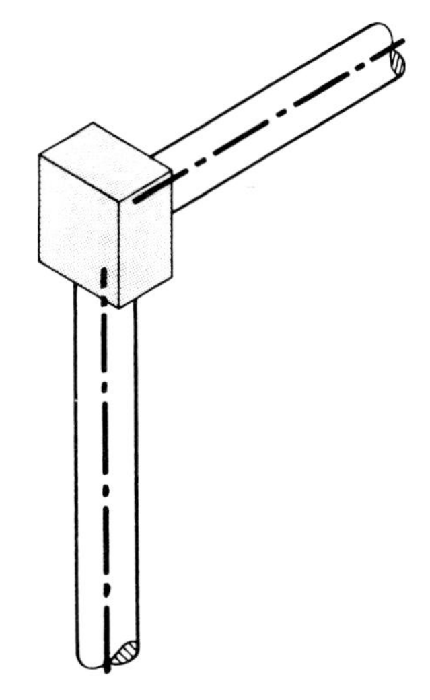

4.5 Intersecting shafts

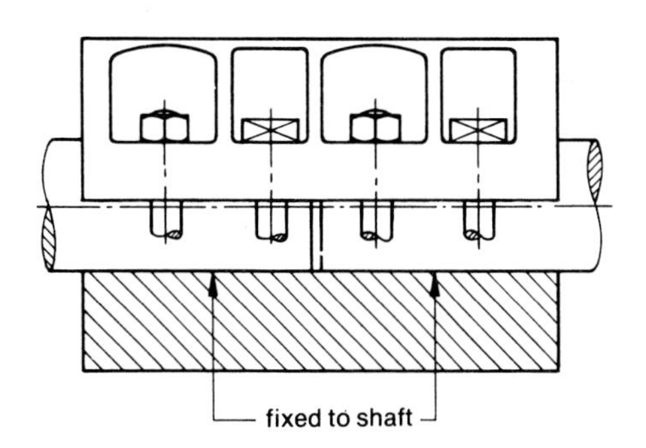

4.6 Permanent coupling-aligned shafts bolted together

4.b Connecting aligned shafts

4.b.i Aligned shafts – transmission ratio 1:1

This group of transmissions includes clutches which are to be divided into:

- permanent couplings (Figs. **4.**6 and **4.**7)
- expansion clutches (Fig. **4.**8)
- dog clutches, cone clutches, plate clutches (Figs. **4.**9, **4.**10 and **4.**11).

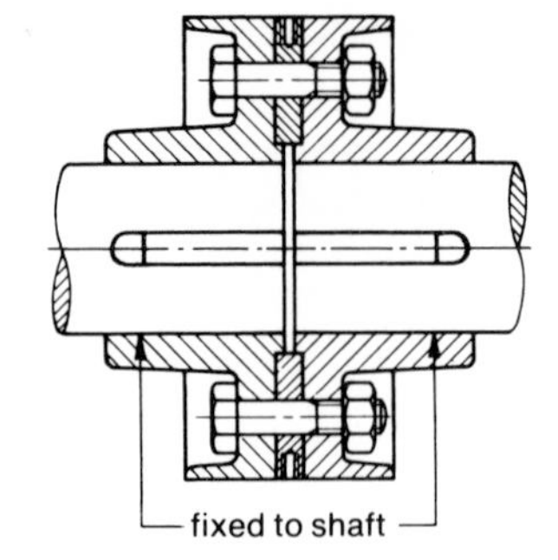

4.7 Permanent coupling

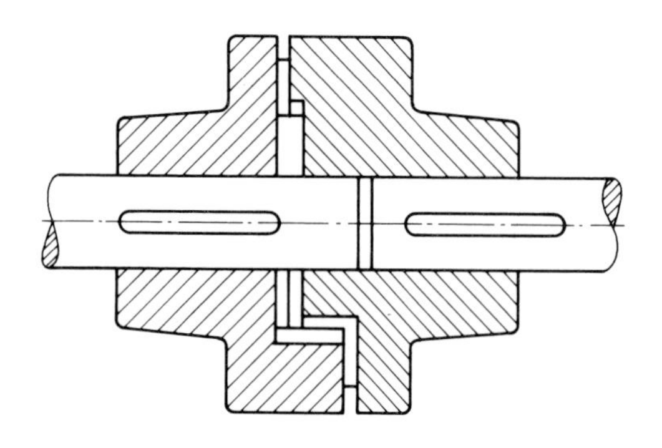

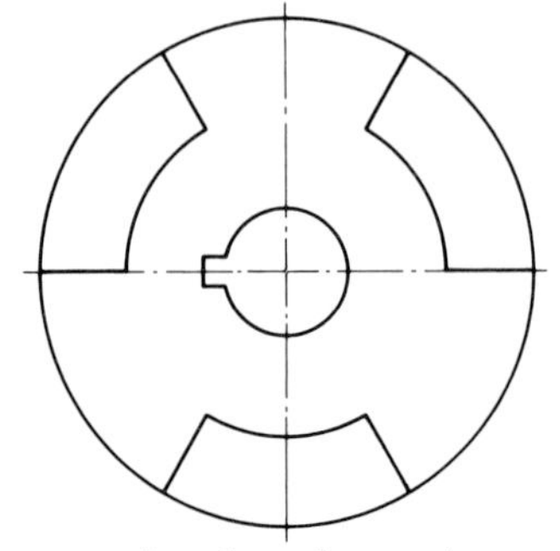

4.8 Expansion clutch

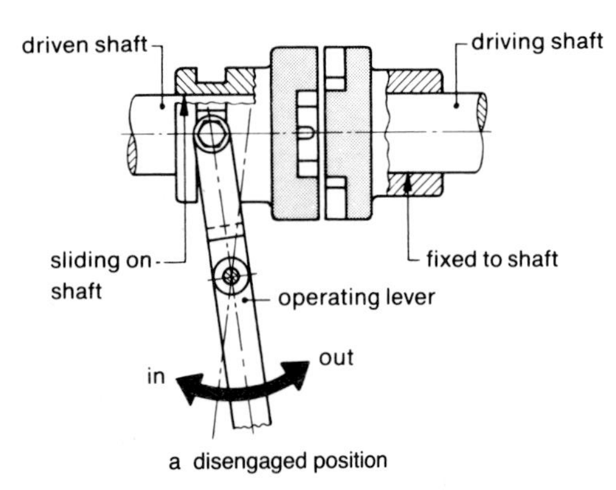

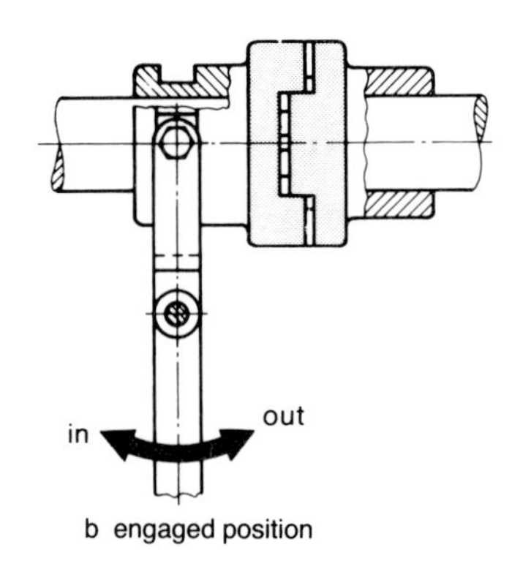

4.9 Dog clutch

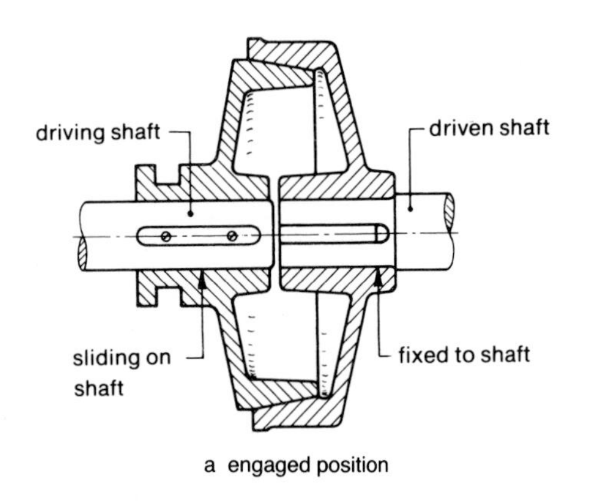

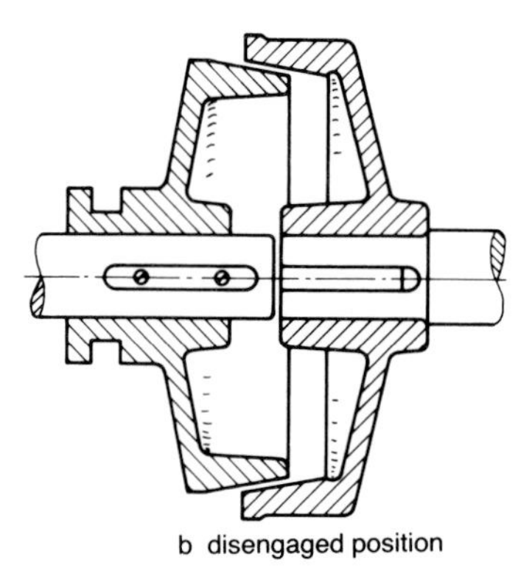

4.10 Friction clutch – cone

- elastic coupling (Figs. **4.**12, **4.**13 and **4.**14)
- safety coupling (Fig. **4.**15).

Fixed couplings are used to connect shaft ends. The contact faces may be either parallel (Fig. **4.**6) or perpendicular to the shafts (Fig. **4.**7)

Clutch: This is a device by which two shafts or rotating members may be connected or disconnected either at rest or during motion.

The dog clutch shown in Fig. **4.**9 can only be engaged when the drive shaft is at a standstill. Cone and plate friction clutches (Figs. **4.**10 and **4.**11) are used to engage or release one shaft while the other is turning. Transmission is achieved by contact between either conical or flat surfaces.

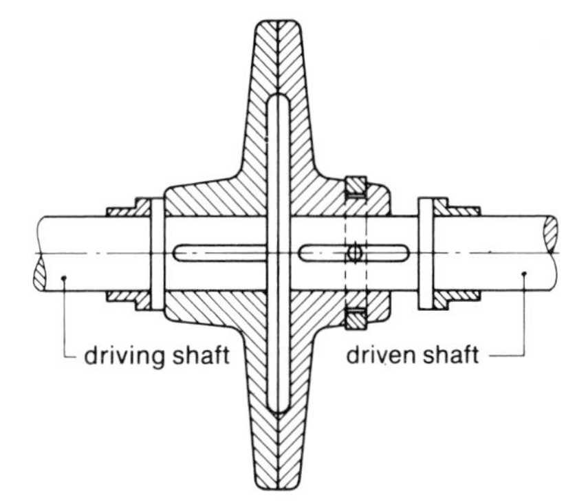

4.11 Friction clutch – disc plate

4.12 Elastic – flexible coupling

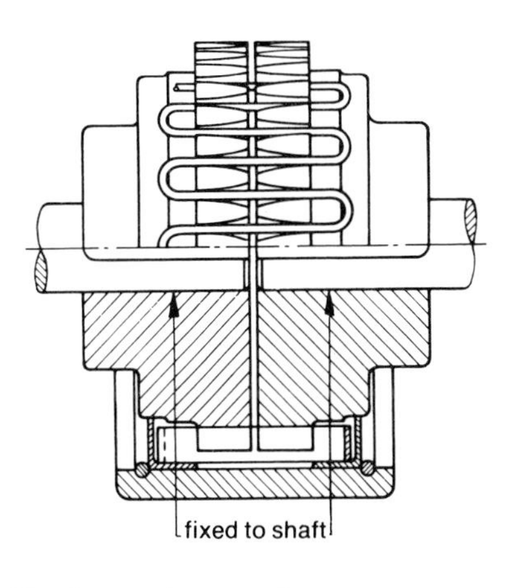

4.13 Elastic – spring coupling

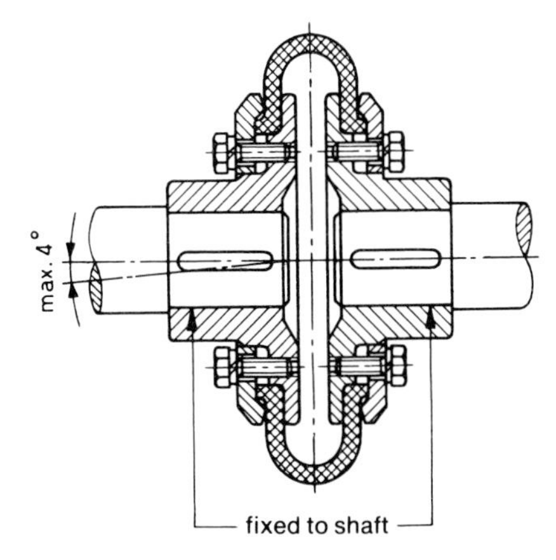

4.14 Elastic – flexible coupling

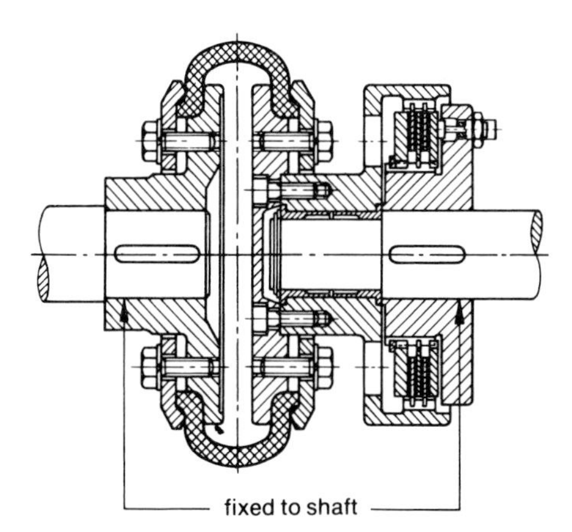

4.15 Safety clutch

Expansion clutches: These are used for long shafts (Fig. **4.**8) to cope with variations in length caused by temperature changes.

Fig. **4.**16 shows the basic clutch of a motor vehicle. The engine is connected to the gearbox via a friction surface (clutch lining). The clutch plate is held away from the rotating engine flywheel whenever the clutch pedal is depressed. As the pedal is allowed to rise the friction surface of the clutch lining is brought into contact with the engine flywheel and the drive to the gearbox via the shaft is taken up. Initially there is some slippage but as the pedal reaches its limit of travel the springs within the clutch overcome the slippage and the clutch plate is held firmly against the rotating flywheel and the drive is completed to the gearbox.

Flexible couplings (Figs. **4.**12, **4.**13 and **4.**14) are capable of absorbing shocks and vibrations. Although slight misalignments of the shafts are permissible, it is recommended that the shafts should be properly aligned when using flexible couplings. The permissible deviation of alignment depends, among other things, on the speed of the shafts.

Overload clutches (Fig. **4.**15). In addition to the establishment of a transmission, these clutches prevent overloading of the shaft or machine. The clutch slips when the maximum permissible load is reached.

4.b.ii Aligned shafts – transmission ratio less than 1:1

The coupled shafts of Figs. **4.**6 to **4.**16 are in line and the transmission ratio is 1:1. The shafts of the mechanisms shown in Figs. **4.**17 and **4.**18 are also in line. However, the transmission ratio here is less than 1:1. A gear transmission has been introduced between the two shafts.

4.c Connecting shafts where centre lines are out of alignment

Where centre lines are out of alignment shafts may be positioned at a slight angle relative to each other. In cases where the shafts are at an angle (maximum 4°), a flexible coupling as shown in Fig. **4.**14 may be used. Certain types of these couplings are also capable of taking up changes in length owing to expansion and slight radial deviations. The flexible portion of the coupling shown in Fig. **4.**14 consists of rubber with canvas inlays.
Figs. **4.**19 and **4.**20 show telescopic shafts using Cardan and Hookes joints.

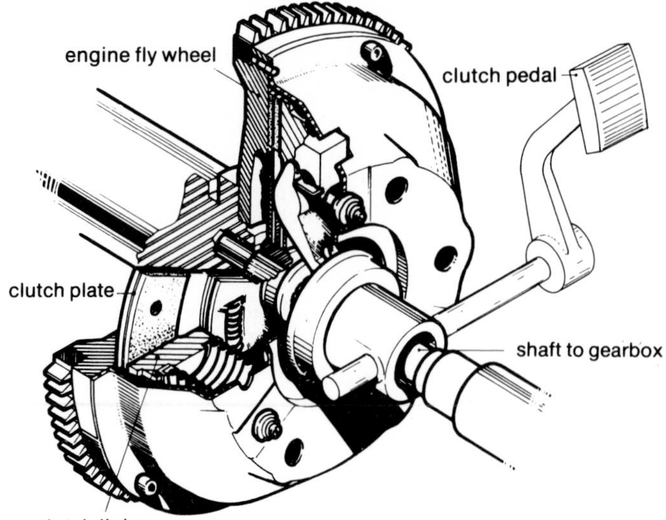

4.16 Motor vehicle clutch (manual)

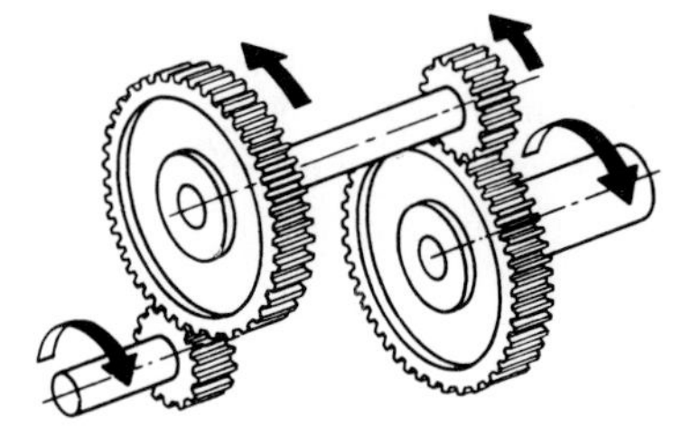

4.17 Gear transmission

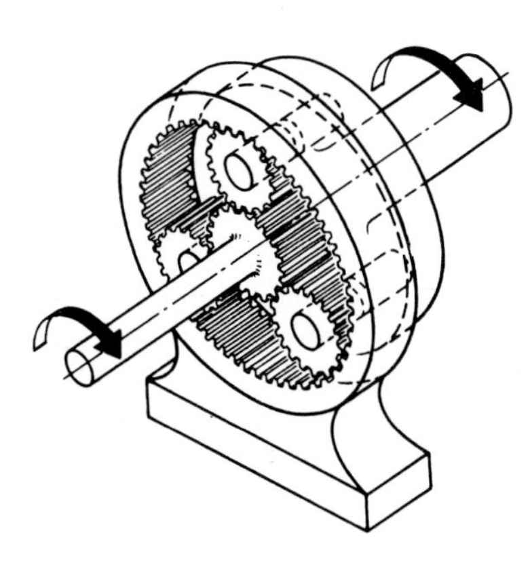

4.18 Gear transmission

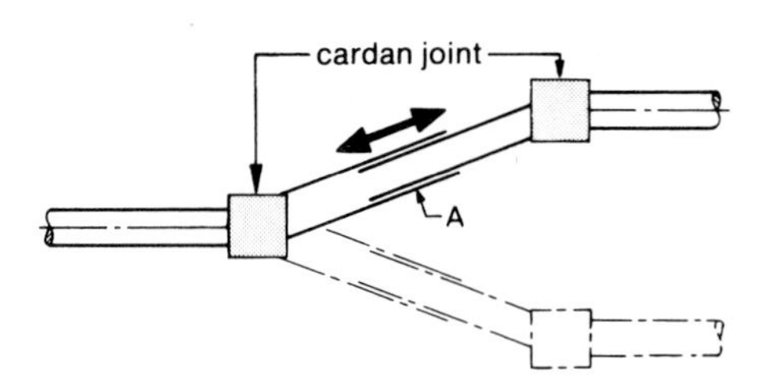

4.19 Telescopic shaft

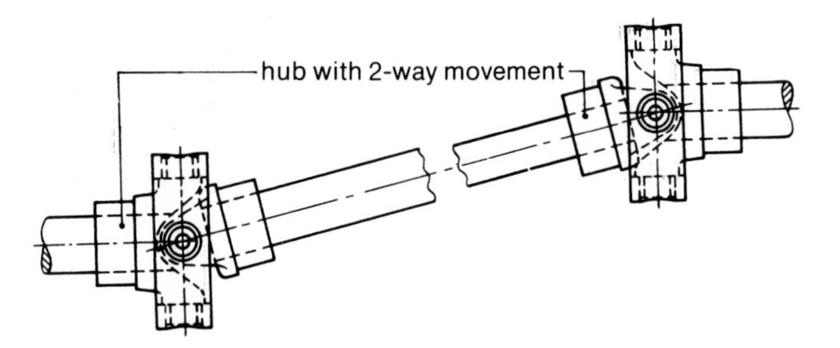

4.20 Double Hookes joints

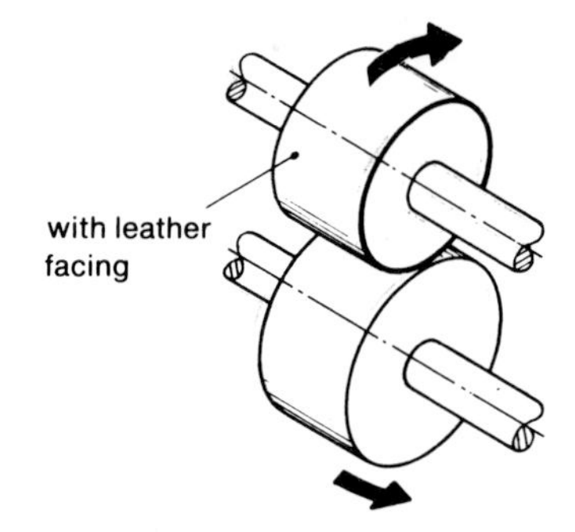

4.21 Friction drive

4.d Connecting parallel shafts

4.d.i to vii Types

Transmission between parallel shafts is widely used. Some types are listed below; they are best understood by careful study of the referenced figures:

- friction wheels (Fig. **4.**21)
- flat belts and pulleys (Fig. **4.**22)
- vee-belts and vee-pulleys (Fig. **4.**23)
- gears (Fig. **4.**24)
- chains and chain wheels (Fig. **4.**25)
- serrated belt and pulley (Fig. **4.**26)
- variators (Fig. **4.**27).

4.d.viii Direction of rotation

The direction of rotation of a transmission may be either:
- the same (Figs. **4.**22 and **4.**23) or
- opposite (Fig. **4.**21).

4.d.ix Slipping and non-slipping transmission

- slipping occurs in friction wheel and belt (flat and vee) transmissions.
- non-slipping transmissions are gear, chain and serrated belt transmissions (Section 6.a.i.).

4.22 Flat belt drive

4.23 Vee-belt transmission

4.24 Gearbox of a turbine

4.25 Chain transmission

4.26 Serrated belt and pulley

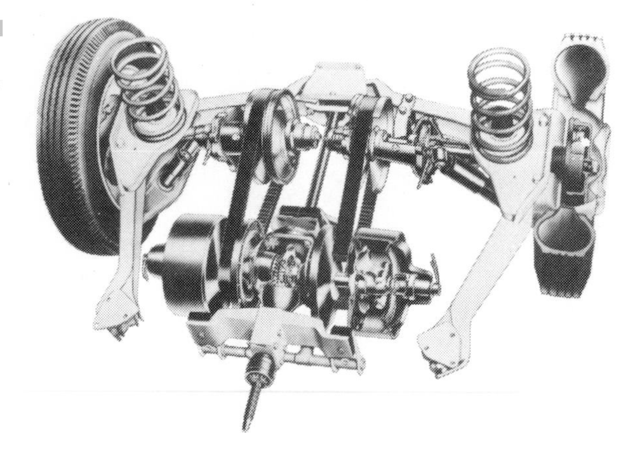

4.27 Variomatic car transmission

4.28 Chain and gear arrangement on a sports cycle

4.d.x Heavy and light duty transmission

- light duty transmission (Fig. **4.**28)
- heavy duty transmission (Fig. **4.**29).

4.e Connecting shafts at 90° in different planes

Transmission between two shafts at 90° in different planes may be established by means of:
i pulleys and belts (Fig. **4.**30)
ii worm and worm gear (Fig. **4.**31)
iii crossed-axis helical gears (Fig. **4.**32)
The angle of the two shafts may be 90° or smaller.

4.29 Vee-belt drive of a large pump

4.30 Belt and pulleys-shafts horizontal-crossing

4.31 Worm and worm gear

4.32 Crossed-axis helical gears

4.f Intersecting shafts

Transmission may be achieved by means of:
i belts and pulleys (Fig. **4.**33)
ii bevel friction drive (Fig. **4.**34)
iii flat friction wheels (Fig. **4.**35)
iv bevel gears (Fig. **4.**36)
v spiral bevel (skew) gears (Fig. **4.**37).
The angle of the axis is usually 90° although transmission between shafts at an angle less than 90° is also possible.

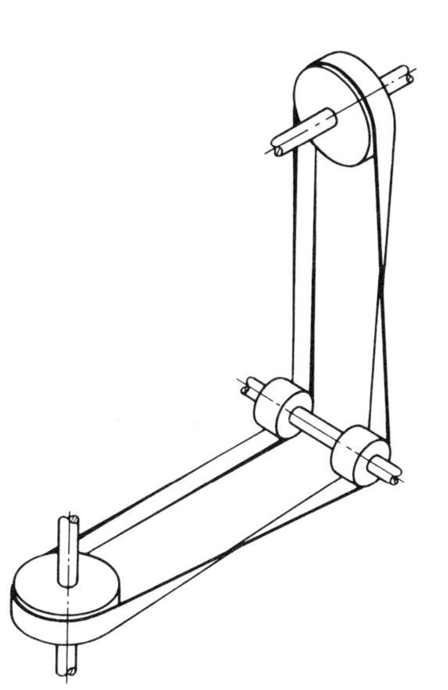

4.33 Belt and pulleys-shafts horizontal and vertical

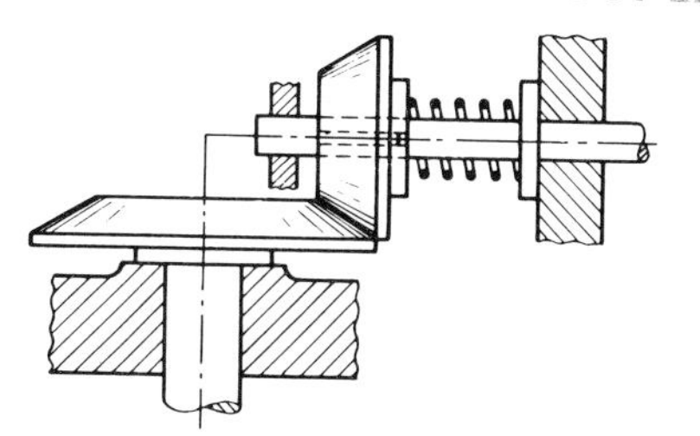

4.34 Bevel friction drive

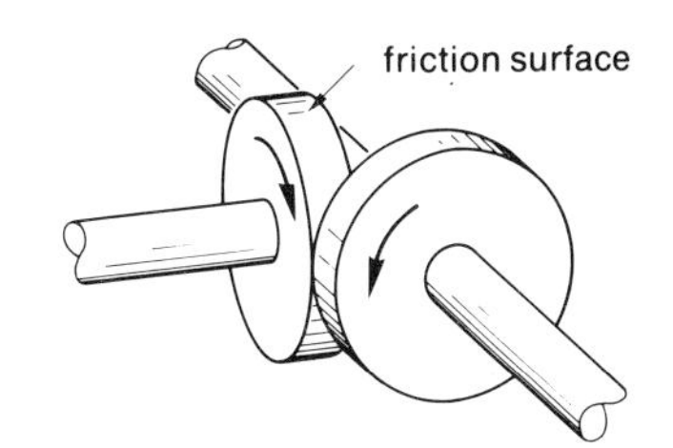

4.35 Flat friction wheel drive

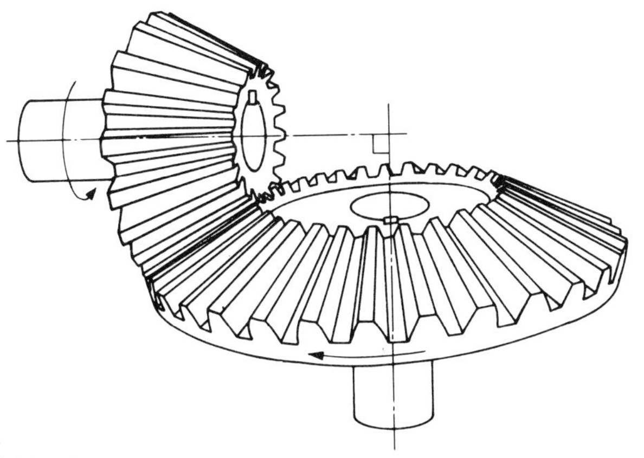

4.36 Straight bevel gears

4.37 Gearbox with spiral bevel gears

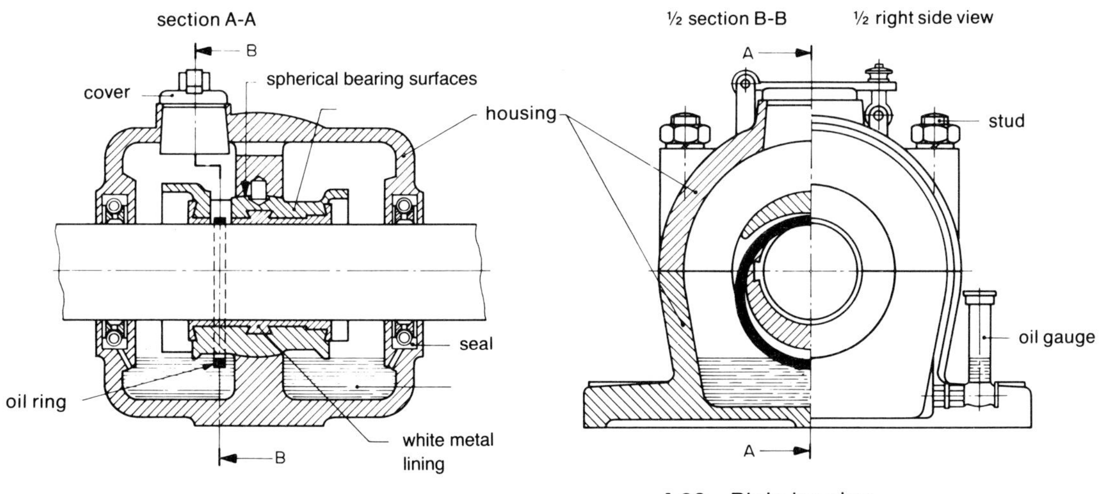

4.38 Plain bearing

4.g Shaft supports

4.g.i Purpose and type of bearings

The purpose of a bearing is to support a rotating shaft in its correct position. Bearings may be of the following type:

- sliding friction bearings – plain bearings (Fig. **4**.38)
- rolling friction bearings – ball, roller or needle bearings (Figs. **4**.39 to **4**.42).

4.39 Roller bearing

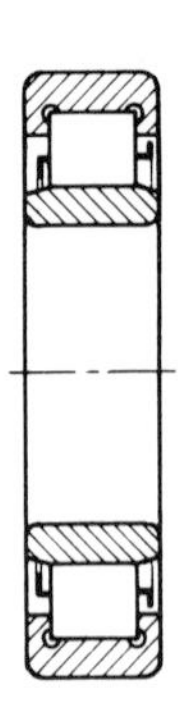

4.40 Ball bearing

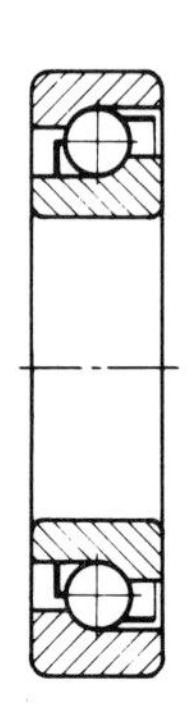

4.41 Roller bearing

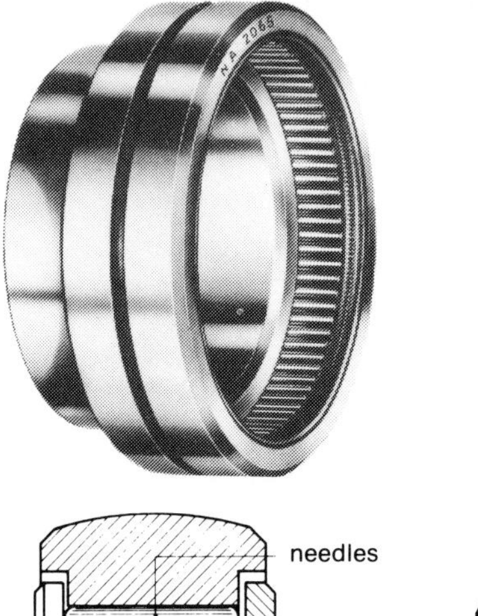

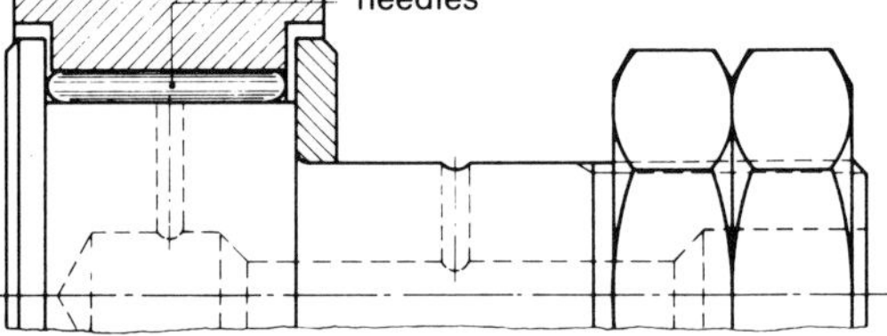

4.42 Needle roller bearing

4.g.i 1 Plain bearings

The materials from which plain bearings are made include:

- bronze, phosphor bronze, oil-retaining sintered bronze
- bronze-lined steel
- white metal lining in cast iron, steel or bronze
- cast iron
- non-metallic.

A plain bearing carrying a radial load as in Fig. **4.**38 is referred to as a journal bearing. That part of the shaft which rests on the bearing is called a journal.

Axial or thrust loads are supported by a thrust bearing, as is a plain bearing headstock of a small lathe.

The simplest form of bearing consists of a cast iron housing with a plain cylindrical hole. With suitable lubrication a steel shaft will run under light loads in this type of bearing for long periods with little wear. The hole may be fitted with a bronze bush, perhaps impregnated with oil and graphite.

The bearing material is usually softer than the shaft, e.g. white metal or phosphor bronze. This reduces damage caused by dirt or dust particles, and confines wear to the bearing, which can be renewed more easily than the shaft. The high crushing loads in automobile practice have resulted in 'thin wall' bearings, in which a thin steel shell is lined with white metal.

The true shape of the bearing is maintained by the use of an accurate bearing housing.

Assembly is facilitated when the housing and bearing are split into two halves; the top or cap is fastened to the base by bolts or studs and may retain a plain or roller bearing. This form of construction is called a pedestal bearing or plummer block (Fig. **4.**39).

Bearing and shaft alignment is achieved by means of a spherical support.

4.g.i 2 Rolling friction bearing – ball, roller and needle

The main advantage of ball and roller bearings is that rolling friction replaces sliding friction. A rolling bearing consists of an inner and outer race, the load carrying balls or rollers, and a cage to keep the balls or rollers apart. Balls, rollers and races are made of alloy steel (ball bearing steel). The most common types of ball and roller bearings are shown in Figs. **4.**39 to **4.**42.

The most often used type of rolling bearing (Fig. **4.**40) is the single row ball bearing which will take both radial and thrust loads in either direction.
Cylindrical roller bearings (Fig. **4.**41) are interchangeable with and have a much greater radial load capacity than the corresponding ball bearing, but they will not withstand end thrust.
Double shoulders on both races will give end-location and resist light thrust loads.
When heavy thrust loads are combined with radial loads, use is made of the taper roller bearing. In this case cylindrical rollers are replaced by taper rollers in tapered races, which have a common apex on the axis of the shaft. These bearings are frequently used in pairs.
Needle roller bearings have cylindrical rollers with a length that is several times their diameter. They are usually made without a cage (Fig. **4.**42) and are often used for oscillating mechanisms and, where space is limited, for low rotational speed applications. End thrust cannot be accommodated by this type of bearing.

4.g.ii Comparison between bearings

In comparing plain and rolling bearings, a major factor is the load to be carried by the bearings. Heavy loads may require plain journal bearings which have the highest load capacity. But these will need a substantial flow of oil. However, damping is good and vibration is minimised. When loading is not so high, rolling bearings may be used. This affects, in particular, the power required to start under load. Lubrication is simpler, and may consist of easily retained grease which requires infrequent replacement. Ball bearings will meet many requirements, but for shock loading and a heavier load the line contact of a roller bearing is preferable to the point contact of a ball bearing.
The length of a rolling bearing is less than that of a plain bearing carrying a similar load. However, rolling bearings are less tolerant of misalignment. Where space is limited to little more than is available for a plain bearing, then a needle roller bearing may be used, in particular for oscillating loads or for low rotational speeds.

5 Characteristics of transmission mechanisms

Transmission mechanisms can be distinguished from one another by a number of characteristic features.

5.a Slip and non-slip transmission systems

Distinction may be made between:
i belts and vee-belts where slippage occurs, and
ii gears, chains and serrated belts which are non-slip transmissions.

5.b Tooth form of gears

5.b.i to iii Tooth geometry

There are several forms of gear tooth geometry:
- gears with straight (spur) teeth (Fig. **5.**1)
- gears with angle helical teeth (Fig. **5.**2)
- gears with double (or triple) helical teeth (Fig. **5.**3).

The shapes of the individual gear teeth can follow two types of curve – the involute curve, much the commonest, and the cycloid curve.

5.b.iv Sideways movement

Gears with straight teeth do not generate sideways pressure, but this pressure is present in helical gears (compare Fig. **5.**1b and Fig. **5.**2b). Gears with double or triple helical teeth are less noisy than straight toothed gears because they mesh with a larger number of teeth. In gears with double or triple helical teeth forces for sideways movement are equal and opposite. Therefore no sideways movement takes place (Fig. **5.**3b).
When considering the choice of gear or belt it should be remembered that:
- flat belts and gears with straight teeth do afford sideways movement (Fig. **5.**4).
- vee-belts and gears with double helical teeth are restrained in their original positions.

5.c Power transmitted

When considering the power which can be transmitted, it should be noted that:
- for low power transmission small profile belts and light gears are used
- high power transmission requires heavy belts and gears.

a illustration

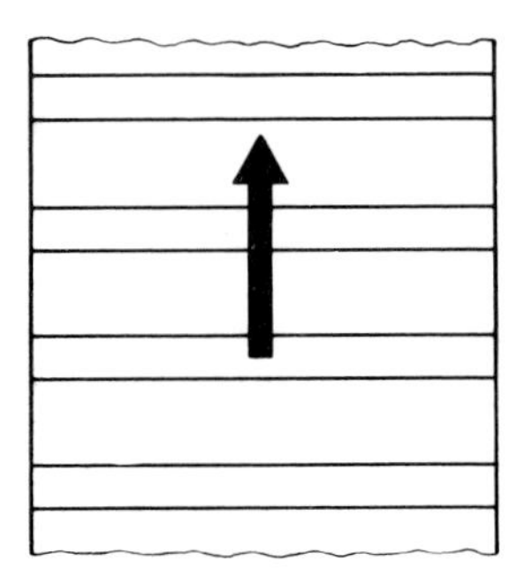

b no sideways pressure

5.1 Gears with straight teeth

a illustration

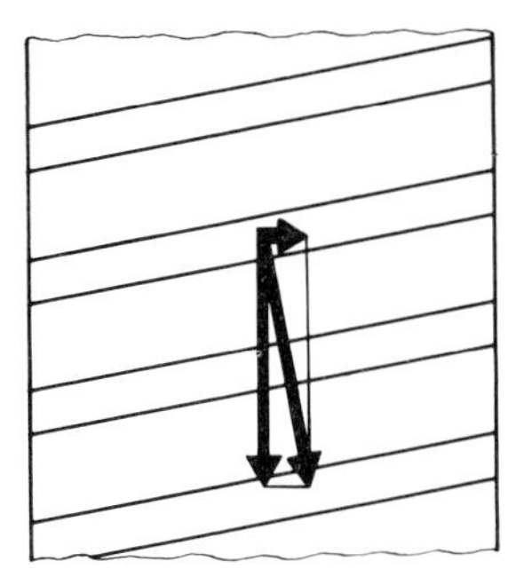

b sideways pressure

5.2 Single helical gear

a illustration

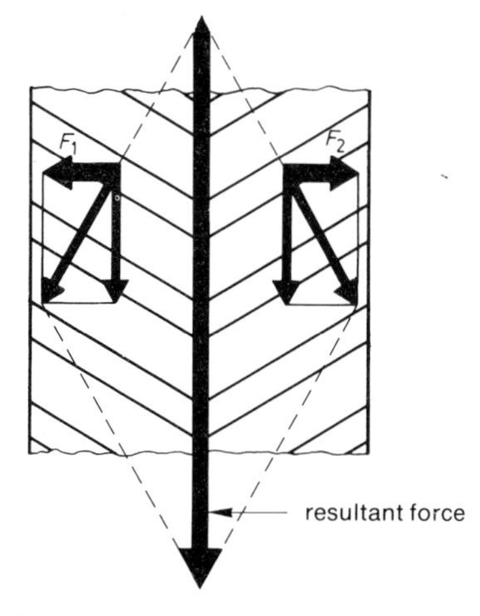

b no sideways pressure

5.3 Double helical gear

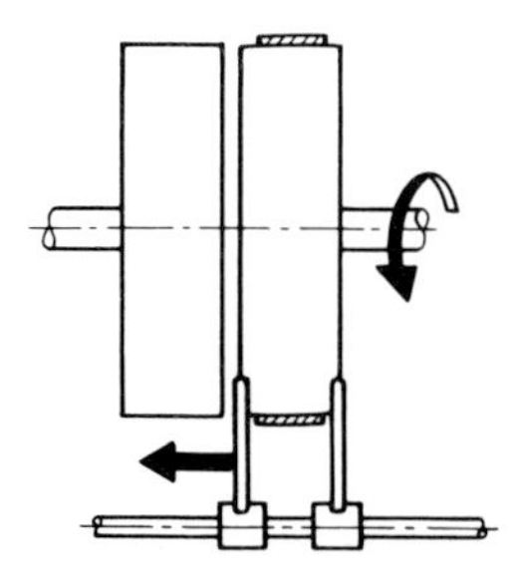

5.4 Sideways movement of a flat belt

6 Advantages and disadvantages of transmission systems

6.a Gears

6.a.i Gear transmission advantages

- The centre distance of the shafts can be small.
- There is no slip (other than the initial take up of tooth clearance).
- Gears with straight teeth and a similar profile can always mesh (as in change gears and quick change gearboxes).
- They can transmit more power than belts.
- They provide a reliable transmission.

6.a.ii Gear transmission disadvantages

- Gear transmission may cause vibration and noise.
- The transmission ratio, $i = \frac{z_1}{z_2}$ (where z_1 and z_2 = the number of teeth of gear 1 and gear 2 respectively) is limited and usually not less than ¼ per transmission.
- Gear transmission is usually more expensive to install and maintain than belt transmission.

6.b Worm gears

6.b.i Worm gear transmission advantages

- Great reductions in a limited space are possible owing to the very low transmission ratio; compare Figs. **6.1** and **6.2**.
- There is no slip.

6.b.ii Worm gear transmission disadvantages

Worm gear transmission has greater frictional losses than spur gear transmission.

6.c Chains

6.c.i Chain drive transmission advantages

- The centre distance of the shafts can be small.
- There is no slipping.
- At equal speeds, the power which can be transmitted by a chain is greater than that by flat or vee-belts.

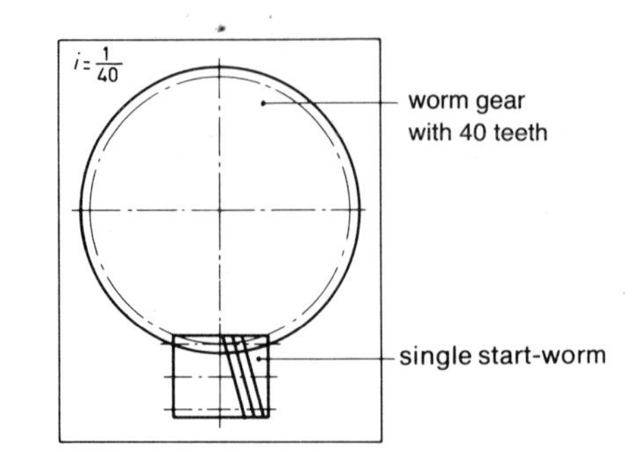

6.1 Worm and worm gear (limited space)

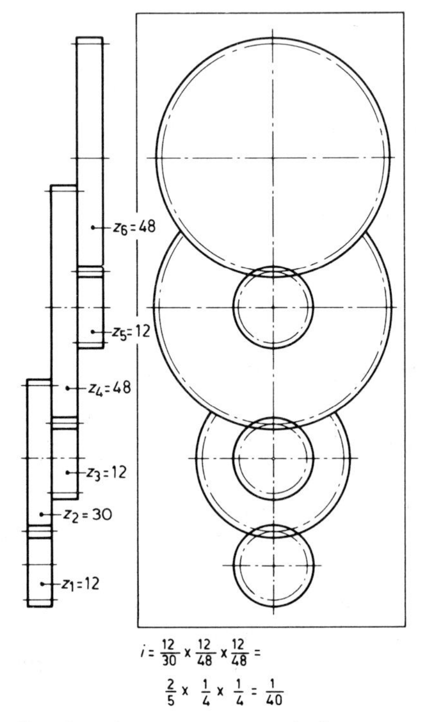

6.2 Gearbox (more space needed)

6.c.ii Chain drive transmission disadvantages

- A chain stretches as a result of normal wear of the link pins. Therefore a chain transmission must be adjustable, e.g. like a bicycle or by an idler chain-wheel which takes up the slack in the chain (Fig. **6.**3).
- The position of the chain-wheels affects the action. For maximum efficiency both shafts should be in the horizontal plane (Fig. **6.**3a) while the least efficient positioning is with the shafts positioned one over the other (Fig. **6.**3b) unless an idler chain wheel (Fig. **6.**3c) is included.

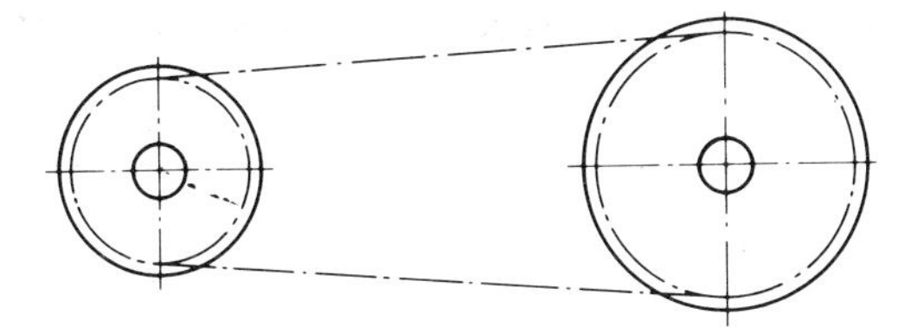

a shafts in horizontal plane

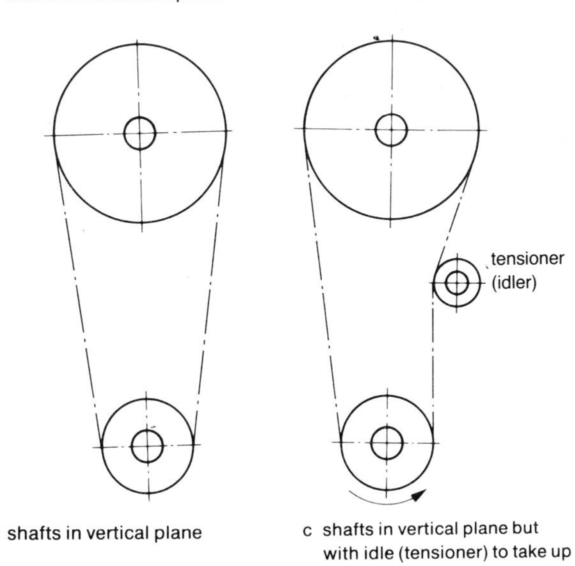

b shafts in vertical plane

c shafts in vertical plane but with idle (tensioner) to take up wear

6.3 Chain drive transmission

6.d Serrated belts

6.d.i Serrated belt transmission advantages

- The centre distance of the shafts can be small.
- There is no slipping as the action is based on meshing.
- The transmission is quiet, even at high speeds.
- High power can be transmitted.
- A good quality serrated belt is almost free from stretch.

6.d.ii Serrated belt transmission disadvantages

Serrated belt transmissions have few disadvantages, because all the favourable qualities of belt, chain and gear transmissions are present.

6.e Flat belts

6.e.i Flat belt transmission advantages

- They can be used as 'open' or 'crossed' transmission.
- They can be moved sideways.
- They are suitable for high velocities, up to 55 m/s.
- They can be easily joined by the use of adhesives.
- They can be shortened.
- Endless belts do not transmit vibrations.

6.e.ii Flat belt transmission disadvantages

- A percentage slip of 1% to 3% must be allowed for when in use.
- Flat belts will stretch during operation and increase the slip factor and vibration.

Note. Endless belts are less noisy and are more suitable for use where high belt speeds are required than are belts that need to be joined.

6.f Vee-belts

6.f.i Vee-belt transmission advantages

- Space saving by using small pulley diameters, small width of pulley (Fig. **6.**4) and short centre distances of the shafts.
- Negligible slippage.
- Vee-belts absorb vibrations and operate silently.
- Belt tension can be less, because the belts tighten themselves in the grooves.
- Shafts and shaft supports are subjected to less loading because of the requirement for less tension.

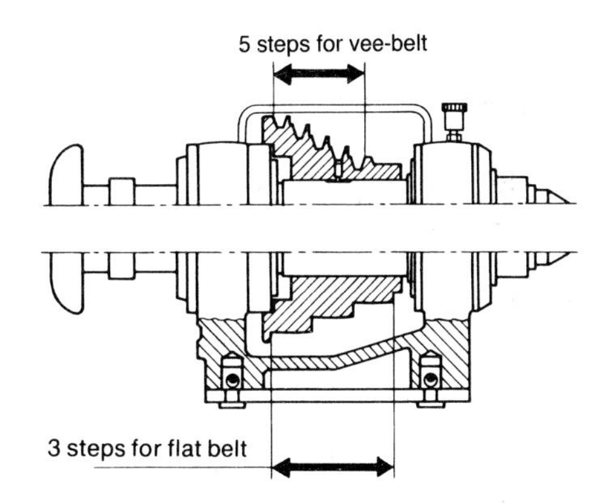

6.4 Advantage of vee over flat belt drive

6.f.ii Vee-belt transmission disadvantages

- Difficult to fit, because vee-belts cannot be moved sideways.
- Vee-belt velocity is limited to 25 m/s.
- Vee-belts stretch in use.
- If one of a set of vee-belts breaks the whole set has to be replaced.

7 Lubrication

7.a Purpose

A lubricating system is required to introduce a substance between two surfaces in relative motion to reduce the friction between them and hence reduce the energy needed to overcome it. Lubrication also minimises wear and increases the performance of a bearing surface.
The principal systems of lubrication either allow the oil to flow into the bearing under gravity or force it under pressure by using a pump. Manually-operated systems of lubrication are often replaced by automatic operation, ensuring that the bearing is not subjected to over or under oiling.

7.b Lubrication systems

7.b.i Hydrodynamic

Hydrodynamic lubrication between two surfaces occurs when they are completely separated by a continuous film of lubricant. Resistance to relative motion is then due only to the viscosity, i.e. the resistance to shear or flow of the film of lubricant and wear of the bearing surfaces is therefore avoided.
Fig. **7.**1 illustrates the movement of the shaft within a bearing and the use of lubricants.
The stationary shaft rests in the bearing as in Fig. **7.**1a. When it reaches normal running speed it takes up the position shown at Fig. **7.**1b and the convergent film of oil creates a hydrodynamic pressure great enough to keep the surfaces apart.
The eccentricity of the shaft in its bearing and the speed needed to generate the hydrodynamic pressure required to carry the load is a disadvantage and may lead to the choice of the hydrostatic bearing.

7.b.ii Hydrostatic

The hydrostatic bearing, more costly than the hydrodynamic system, avoids metal-to-metal contact when starting from rest and can be made to retain a constant axis of rotation under varying load (Fig. **7.**1c). The pressure required to support the load is provided by an externally pumped oil supply.

Note. The clearances shown in the diagrams are greatly exaggerated.

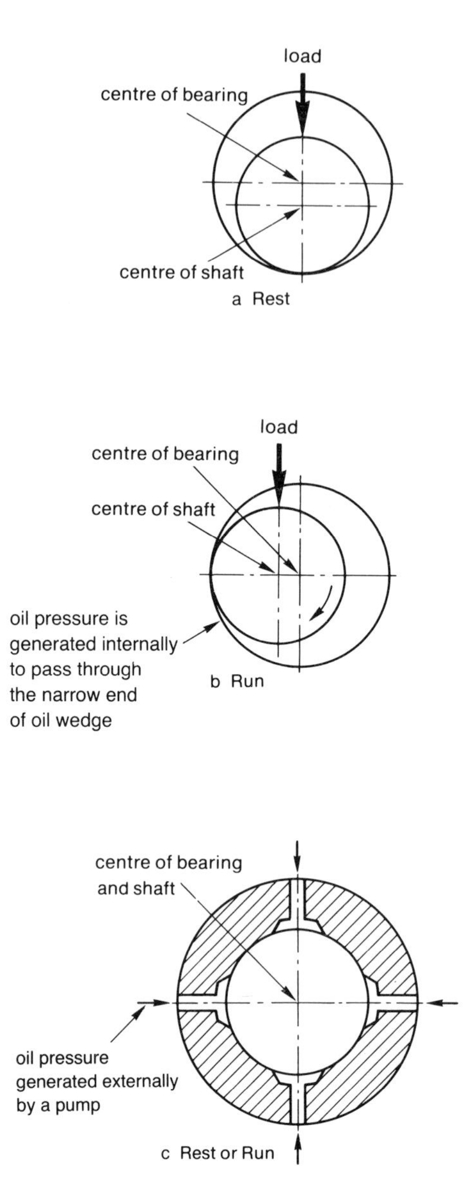

7.1 Hydrodynamic and hydrostatic lubrication

7.c Classification of lubricants

Lubricants are usually classified according to their viscosity (resistance to flow, or 'thickness'), which is their most significant parameter. The viscosity numbers devised by the Society of Automotive Engineers of America (SAE) are the most commonly used classification system. A low number indicates a 'thin' oil and a high number indicates a 'thick' oil. The SAE system was originally introduced for automobile use. The International Organisation for Standardisation (ISO) system is also used to classify industrial lubricants in ISO viscosity grades.

7.c.i Oils

General-purpose mineral oils give excellent lubrication in plain bearings, provided that a suitable viscosity is chosen, and that due attention is given to such factors as the speed of operation, the expected temperature rise in the bearing, and the type of lubrication.
A rise in temperature reduces the viscosity of most oils, and a *viscosity index* (VI) is used to indicate the effect of temperature.
The index is based on the variation in viscosity with the temperature of two standard oils. A high viscosity index indicates a small change in viscosity with temperature.
The load-carrying capacity of an oil film increases with the viscosity, and this ranges from the low-viscosity lubricating oils used for lightly loaded spindles, which avoid high bearing temperatures, to the high-viscosity oils needed to carry the load between the meshing teeth of gears. The teeth tend to squeeze out the oil and additives are used in gear oils to meet this problem.
A rise in pressure produces an increase in viscosity, but if the pressure between the bearing surfaces increases to too high a level there will eventually be a breakdown in the oil film, and some metal-to-metal contact occurs. Certain substances add the property of 'oiliness' to mineral oil, and the 'boundary' film which results provides lubrication under high pressures and low speeds.
Severe friction requires a very special boundary lubricant of the 'extreme pressure' type (EP). This includes an additive based on sulphur, phosphorus or chlorine, and produces a protective film on metal surfaces at the high temperatures resulting from high pressures, where normal lubricants break down.

7.c.ii Greases

Greases are semi-solid materials composed of mineral oils, usually thickened with a metallic soap and often with other additives, which, for example, may increase the load-carrying properties.
Grease is usually classified by its 'consistency' using the system of the National Lubricating Grease Institute (NLGI). This measures the depth of penetration of a standard cone into a grease during a period of five seconds. The higher the NLGI number, the stiffer the grease.
A lithium thickened multi-purpose grease of NLGI number 2 or 3 is used extensively for general lubrication. It has good water-resistance and a recommended operating temperature of over 100°C.
For temperatures to 200°C bentonite base greases are used; they are also water-resistant.
However, where temperatures do not exceed about 60°C a calcium base provides a grease which is very resistant to water. Where temperatures are very low a calcium base grease may be used down to −40°C.
Some greases contain solid lubricants such as graphite or molybdenum disulphide. These are not used for high-speed operation, but improve the load-carrying properties under very hot conditions. They are generally used with plain bearings.

7.d Properties of lubricants

7.d.i Viscosity

Viscosity is that property of a lubricating oil which provides resistance to flow. Viscosity falls with an increase in temperature and rises with an increase in pressure.

7.d.ii Film strength

Film strength is that pressure which a film of lubricating oil or grease can support without breakdown when subjected to standard test conditions.

7.d.iii Storage

Lubricating oils should be stored away from possible contamination by dust and/or water. Extremes of temperature are to be avoided. Greases may be stored in dry conditions for several years without deterioration but they will be adversely affected by excessive heat.

7.e Applications

In addition to the normal functions of reducing friction and wear, lubricants used in ball and roller bearings protect the highly finished surfaces from corrosion. Furthermore, at high operating speeds lubricants carry away heat and keep the bearings at a uniform working temperature.
Experience shows that although oil is the better lubricant, grease is often preferred because it has many advantages. Grease provides an effective means of closing the gap existing between a rotating shaft and its housing, thereby preventing the entry of dirt, moisture and other harmful substances. Grease clings to stationary surfaces better than oil, which drains away. Hence grease provides protection from corrosion more effectively than oil. Similarly grease is easier to retain within a bearing housing than oil. This is of great importance in the food, printing, textile, chemical and similar industries where contamination or staining can ruin a product.

7.f Types of lubrication system

A lubricant cannot function effectively unless it is applied in a reliable manner. The earliest method of application was by the use of an oil-can, but the quantity applied and the frequency of application varies.
A reservoir of some form, fitted with a simple feed system, provides a more constant supply.

7.f.i Gravity and wick drip

The simplest type of feed is the drip lubricator in which a needle controls the rate of oil flow from a glass container.
A wick syphon feed lubricator leads oil from the reservoir to the bearing by means of the wick.

7.f.ii Ring

Ring oiling employs a loose ring resting on the bearing shaft, and dipping into a reservoir of oil. Rotation of the shaft carries the ring round with it, and the oil adhering to the ring is spread over the shaft and into the bearing.

7.f.iii Splash

Splash feed is frequently used for gear drives; the lowest gear runs in an oil bath. Oil is carried by the gear teeth to the point of mesh of the gears.

7.f.iv Spray

High gear speeds tend to throw off the oil and the splash feed system is replaced by the system in which oil is sprayed on to the gears.

7.f.v Mist

Mist lubrication uses air under pressure to carry oil as a mist to the bearings. This avoids the loss of power which an excess of oil may produce, quite unnecessarily in the case of rolling bearings. The air helps to cool the bearing, and since the air in the bearing housing is normally above atmospheric pressure, it prevents the entry of dirt or dust.

7.f.vi Circulation

A circulation system draws oil from a reservoir by means of a pump and distributes it through pipework to bearings and gears. The oil then drains back to the reservoir for recirculation. Oil mist lubrication can also be applied by a central circulatory system.

8 Seals

8.a Purpose

The function of a seal is to prevent the passage of a fluid or a gas from a location in which it is normally confined into a location where its properties are not required or where it is lost.

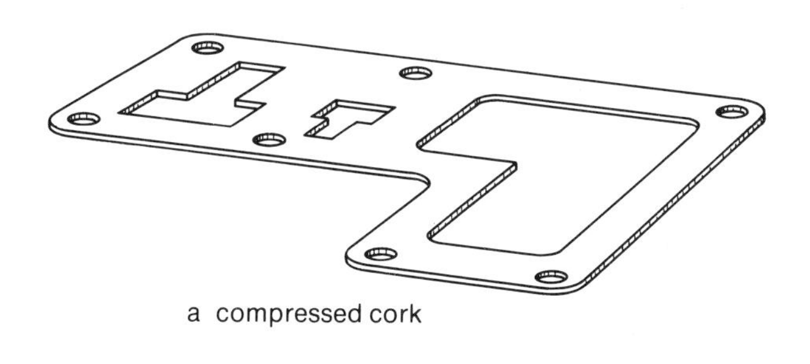

a compressed cork

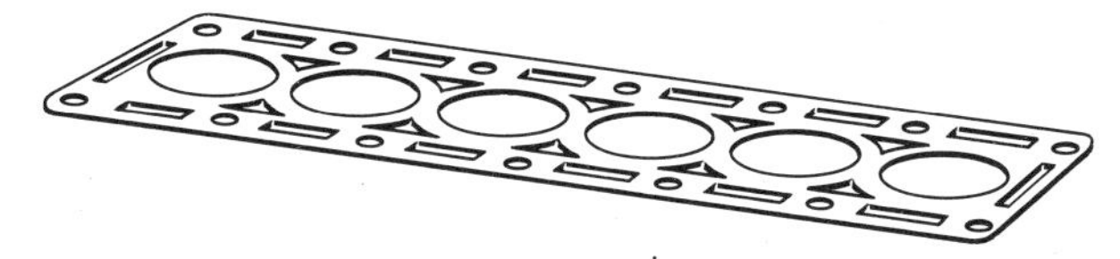

b soft metal sandwich (cylinder head gasket)

8.1 Static seals

8.b Static and dynamic seals

Seals may be classified as static or dynamic:

- *Static seal* – one that provides a seal between two stationary objects, e.g. a cylinder head gasket of an internal combustion machine.
- *Dynamic seal* – one that provides a seal between two objects that move relative to each other, e.g. the oil seal surrounding an engine crankshaft at the point where it passes, via a bearing, through the engine block.

8.c Common types of seal

There are several types of seal:

- *Compressed cork* – a static seal used in relatively low pressure applications (Fig. **8.**1a).
- *Soft metal* – a static seal, normally a copper aluminium sandwich used in high pressure, high temperature applications (Fig. **8.**1b).
- *O Ring* – a dynamic seal made of synthetic rubber, one of the most economic forms of seal. Rubber can be considered to be incompressible and when squeezed on one plane must be allowed to deflect in another plane (Fig. **8.**2a).
- *Bonded seal* – a dynamic seal used for high-pressure applications. It comprises a metal annulus of square or rectangular section to which an elastomeric ring of trapezoidal section is bonded (Fig. **8.**2b).
- *U Packing* – a dynamic seal made of synthetic rubber. Used in many low and medium pressure applications (Fig. **8.**2c).

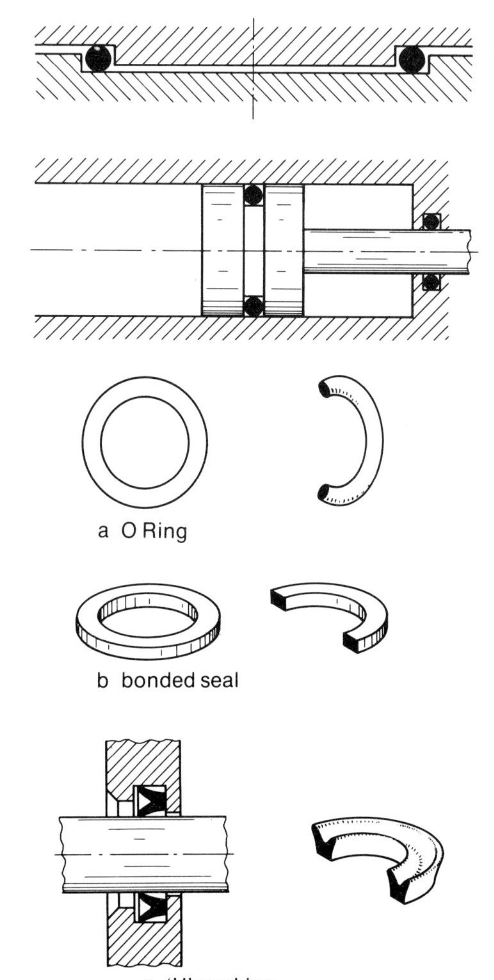

a O Ring

b bonded seal

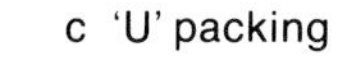

c 'U' packing

8.2 Types of dynamic seal

8.d Applications of static and dynamic seals

Table 8.1 Seals and their applications

Type of seal	Static	Dynamic	Application
Compressed cork	x		Engine rocker cover. Cooling systems (low pressure). Distributor body seal.
Soft metal sandwich	x		Cylinder head gaskets. High pressure glands. Glands subject to high temperature.
O Ring		x	Distributor shaft seal. Brake master cylinder seal.
Bonded seal		x	High pressure hydraulic/ pneumatic applications.
U packing		x	Medium pressure hydraulic/ pneumatic applications.

9 Safety

Machinery in motion is a serious hazard. Stringent safety precautions must be observed at all times. Some of the basic precautions relating to machinery are listed below. Further information on safety can be found in the series book *Observing Safe Practices and Moving Loads*.

a Great care must be taken when working with machinery where parts in motion are exposed, i.e. lathes, milling machines and grinding machines.
b Isolating switches for individual machines must be within easy reach of the machinery operator standing in the normal operating position.
c Belt shifting slides must be fastened in their extreme position.
d Spoked pulleys must be guarded when within hand reach.
e Gears, chains, rotating shafts, couplings and feed mechanisms must be caged.

The measures listed above may be classified as technical measures. Although these measures are important in themselves, the operator's personal attitude towards safety in general is of much greater importance. The following points should be noted:

f Never wear loose clothing near moving machinery, e.g. scarves, loose ties, chains, beads or bangles.
g Always keep long hair tucked up under a hat.
h When minding a machine in an automatic mode, never be tempted to leave the machine unattended or prop a book up on the casing and read.

Technology of Skilled Processes

Basic Engineering
Competences 201

Power Transmission

Practice and test questions

Published as a
co-operative venture
between
Stam Press Ltd

and

**City and Guilds of
London Institute**

Practice and test questions

The questions in this book are intended to help the student achieve and demonstrate a knowledge and understanding of the subject matter covered by this book. Accordingly, the questions follow the original chapter order, under the same headings. Finally there are questions spanning the chapters and approximating to the level of those in the relevant examination of the City and Guilds of London Institute.

Australia AEP, Blackburn (Melbourne)
België Plantyn, Deurne (Antwerpen)
Belgique Plantyn, Bruxelles
BRD Stam, Köln
France Casteilla/Educalivre, Paris
Great Britain **Stam Press, Cheltenham**
Stanley Thornes, Cheltenham
Nederland Educaboek, Culemborg
Educa Int., Culemborg
De Ruiter, Gorinchem
Suisse Delta & Spes, Denges (Lausanne)

First published in Great Britain 1987
as a co-operative venture between Stam Press Ltd
and the City and Guilds of London Institute

Reprinted 1991

Printed in Great Britain by Martin's of Berwick.

POWER TRANSMISSION Name: ______________________ Class: __________ Number: ______

1 Introduction to transmission mechanisms

The following questions relate to the above aspects of power transmission, but what is stated here about answering them *also* applies to similarly framed questions covering later subject headings.
Many questions, as in 1.1 – 1.5 provide a number of possible answers, usually four, lettered a, b, c and d. Unless otherwise stated, only *one* answer is correct. You have to decide which it is and indicate by circling the appropriate letter(s) or number(s).

Example
Rectilinear motion is:
a movement in a right turning arc
b movement oscillating about a straight line
ⓒ movement in a straight line
d movement in a circle

Where a written answer is required, this should be short and clear; where a sketch or diagram is required, this should be clear and adequately labelled.

---

1 In a drilling machine, the arrangement for transmitting the rotational motion of the electric motor to the drilling spindle is called a:
a feed mechanism
b transmission mechanism
c control mechanism
d conversion mechanism

---

2 The SI unit of length is the:
a kilometre
b metre
c centimetre
d millimetre

---

3 During drilling the corner of the cutting edge of a drill makes a movement described as:
a arbitrary motion
b rectilinear motion
c circular motion
d helical motion

---

4 During grinding the motion of point A on the circumference of a grinding wheel shown in the figure is described as:
a arbitrary motion
b rectilinear motion
c circular motion
d helical motion

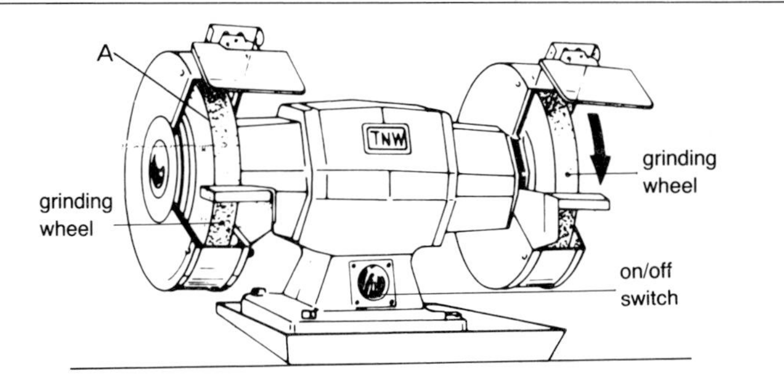

---

5 The SI unit of velocity is the:
a kilometre per hour
b metre per hour
c metre per second
d millimetre per second

---

6 Give THREE examples where mechanisms are applied.

____

____

____

____

 Name: ____________ Class: ________ Number: _____

7 Name the SI units used as a measure of peripheral velocity.

8 Name the type of motion produced by a point on the circumference of a revolving pulley.

9 Illustrate with a simple sketch the difference between continuous and intermittent motions.

2 Applications

The following questions relate to the above subject. Except where otherwise indicated, the correct answers should be given as explained on page 41.

1 Describe the purpose of a coupling mechanism.

2 Sketch the chain drive transmission of a bicycle.

3 Sketch the conversion mechanism of a power hacksaw.

 Name: ______________________ Class: __________ Number: _____

4 Sketch the conversion mechanism of a rack and pinion drive.

---

5 Sketch the transmission mechanism between two four step vee-belt pulleys, using a single vee-belt.

---

6 Sketch a mechanism used for reversing the direction of rotation of a machine by means of toothed wheels.

---

7 State the purpose of locking and interlocking mechanisms.

____
____
____
____

---

8 Make a simple sketch showing how a linear motion in the cylinder is converted to the rotary motion of the shaft in the internal combustion engine.

---

9 List THREE uses of control mechanisms.

____
____
____
____

---

10 Sketch and describe the principle of operation of a hydraulic jack.

____
____
____
____

POWER TRANSMISSION Name: ______________________ Class: __________ Number: _____

3 Operating principles of transmission systems

The following questions relate to the above subject. Except where otherwise indicated, the correct answers should be given as explained on page 41.

1 The transmission arrangement used to obtain a friction drive between two shafts is:
- a a vee-belt and vee-pulley
- b a serrated belt and pulley
- c a worm and wormwheel
- d crossed axis helical gears

2 The vee-belt is most suitable for transmission between shafts which are:
- a intersecting
- b parallel
- c crossed
- d meeting at any angle

3 Straight bevel gear wheels are most suitable for transmission between shafts which are:
- a intersecting
- b parallel
- c crossed
- d meeting at any angle

4 Identify the transmission system which has infinite adjustable speed variation within limits:
- a flat belt and pulley
- b vee-belt
- c a variator
- d gear wheels

5 The transmission which is entirely without friction is:
- a gear wheels
- b worm and wormwheel
- c a non-existent condition
- d helical gears

6 Give THREE examples of a drive with a fixed transmission ratio.

____

____

____

____

7 Sketch a variator drive.

8 Sketch a single transmission using toothed wheels.

 Name: ______ Class: ______ Number: ______

9 Sketch a double transmission using toothed wheels.

10 Give THREE examples of mechanisms with fixed and adjustable transmission ratios.

11 State the methods of transmission which are classified as non-slipping.

12 Sketch examples of mechanisms, one with a transmission ratio of 1:1, and one with a transmission ratio less than 1:1.

4 Shaft position

The following questions relate to the above subject. Except where otherwise indicated, the correct answers should be given as explained on page 41.

1 List the methods available for providing transmission between intersecting shafts.

2 State how transmission between crossed shafts is achieved.

3 State the reason why a dog clutch, which is used with revolving shafts, can be engaged only when the drive shaft is at a standstill.

4 Two aligned shafts are subjected to vibration. Which type of coupling should be used to connect these shafts?

5 Two long aligned shafts are subjected to temperature variation. Which type of coupling should be used to join these shafts together?

6 State the circumstances in which a safety coupling should be used.

7 Sketch flexible coupling

8 Sketch an expansion coupling.

9 State the types of bearing used to support and guide moving shafts.

10 List the material used in the manufacture of plain bearings.

11 In what circumstances would taper roller bearings be used?

12 State the reason why a bearing material is usually softer than the shaft that runs in the bearing.

13 What are 'thin wall' bearings, and why are they used?

14 Sketch and describe a plummer block.

15 Sketch one type of self-aligning bearing.

16 State the advantages of ball and roller bearings compared with plain bearings.

17 Sketch the most common type of ball and roller bearings.

18 How are combined radial and thrust loads resisted in a roller bearing?

19 Describe the difference between journal and thrust bearings.

20 Where would needle roller bearings be used? What is their disadvantage?

 Name: ______________________ Class: __________ Number: ______

21 How is the choice of the type of bearing influenced by the load to be carried by the bearing?

22 State the type of bearing that offers least resistance to starting under load.

23 Which type of rolling friction bearing would be most suitable for shock loading?

5 Characteristics of transmission mechanisms

The following questions relate to the above subject. Except where otherwise indicated, the correct answers should be given as explained on page 41.

1 Slip can occur in one of the following means of transmission:
a serrated belts
b worm and wormwheel
c crossed axis helical gears
d vee-belts

2 In the transmission systems listed, slip will not occur with:
a serrated belts
b friction wheels
c flat belts
d vee-belts

3 Gears with a double helical form are less noisy than gears with straight teeth. This is because:
a there is no sideways pressure produced
b they produce a sideways pressure
c there are more teeth engaged at the same time
d there is only one tooth engaged at a time

4 Show, by means of a sketch, that in the case of gear wheels with straight teeth, no sideways pressure occurs.

 Name: ______ Class: ______ Number: ______

5 Show, by means of a sketch, that gear wheels with helical teeth produce a sideways pressure.

6 Show, by means of a sketch, that in the case of double helical gears there is no resultant sideways pressure.

7 State the type of transmission used for:
a low power
b high power

8 Describe the difference between slip and non-slip transmission systems.

6 Advantages and disadvantages of transmission systems

The following questions relate to the above subject. Except where otherwise indicated, the correct answers should be given as explained on page 41.

1 List the advantages and disadvantages of a transmission using gears.

2 Explain the advantages and disadvantages of a transmission using a worm and wormwheel.

3 Discuss the advantages and disadvantages of a transmission using a chain and chain-wheel.

 Name: ________ Class: ________ Number: ________

4 What are the advantages of a transmission using a flat belt and pulley?

5 List the advantages and disadvantages of a transmission using a vee-belt and pulleys.

6 What are the advantages of endless belts over those which have to be joined?

7 List the advantages and disadvantages of serrated belt drives.

8 Use a sketch to show that a transmission using a vee-belt drive requires less width than the equivalent drive using a flat belt.

7 Lubrication systems

The following questions relate to the above subject. Except where otherwise indicated, the correct answers should be given as explained on page 41.

1 Explain the reasons for the use of a lubricating system.

2 List the principal methods of lubrication.

3 Explain why manual systems of lubrication may be replaced by automatic operation.

 Name: ______ Class: ______ Number: ______

4 Describe, using simple sketches, the principle of hydrodynamic lubrication.

5 State when a hydrostatic bearing would be used.

6 Indicate the most significant factor used to describe a lubricant.

7 Explain how the SAE classification system is applied to lubricants.

8 Name the property of an oil indicated by the viscosity index.

9 Explain how the load-carrying capacity of an oil film is influenced by its viscosity.

10 State what causes the breakdown of the oil film in a bearing, and describe the result.

11 Describe where an extreme pressure lubricant would be used and state the effect of additives in this lubricant.

12 Explain how greases are classified.

 Name: ______________ Class: ________ Number: _____

13 Name the purpose for which solid lubricants are added to some greases.

14 Describe the conditions required for the storage of lubricating oils and greases.

15 Give the factors that are considered in the selection of a suitable lubricant for a plain journal bearing.

16 Describe the advantages and disadvantages of using oil or grease in the lubrication of rolling bearings.

17 Describe the characteristics needed for a suitable lubricant for use in a gearbox.

18 Sketch and describe drip and siphon feed lubricators.

19 Sketch the principle of ring oiling.

20 Explain when splash feed lubrication is used and give its main disadvantages.

21 Describe the advantages of using mist lubrication.

8 Seals

The following questions relate to the above subject. Except where otherwise indicated, the correct answers should be given as explained on page 41.

1 State the function of a seal.

2 Describe the difference between static and dynamic seals.

3 State where you would expect to find a compressed cork seal.

4 Name the material which would be used for a static seal required in a high-pressure, high-temperature application.

5 Describe how an 'O Ring' provides a seal between fixed and moving parts.

6 Describe the construction of a gasket suitable for the cylinder head of an internal combustion engine.

7 Explain how high-pressure sealing would be achieved between moving parts.

POWER TRANSMISSION Name: ______ Class: ______ Number: ______

9 Safety

The following questions relate to the above subject. Except where otherwise indicated, the correct answers should be given as explained on page 41.

---

1 State THREE basic precautions to be observed when working with power transmission machinery.

______

______

______

---

2 What precautions related to their clothing and appearance should be observed by machine operatives?

______

______

______

______

POWER TRANSMISSION Name: ______________________ Class: __________ Number: _____

The following questions span the subject matter and approximate to those in the relevant examination paper of the City and Guilds of London Institute. Answers should be short and clear.

1 Define a power transmission system. Give two examples.

2 Define acceleration. How is acceleration measured and what is the SI unit used?

3 Define helical motion. Give an example.

4 With the aid of a diagram explain how the burning gases in the cylinder of an internal combustion engine produce a rotary motion in a shaft.

5 Explain with the aid of a diagram how a reversing mechanism works.

6 Give THREE examples of a friction drive.

7 Sketch a 'rack and pinion'.

8 What is meant by the transmission ratio of a series of gears?

9 State the limitation in the use of a dog clutch.

10 In what circumstances is an expansion clutch used?

11 With the aid of a diagram explain how the speed of a shaft can be varied by using a friction drive from another shaft positioned on the same plane but at 90° to it.

12 State THREE methods of connecting shafts intersecting at 90° but on different planes.

13 What is the purpose of a bearing?

14 Explain what is meant by the term 'thin wall bearing'.

15 State the differences between journal and thrust bearings.

16 With the aid of a diagram explain how sideways movement in a double helical gear is prevented.

17 State the main disadvantages with a chain transmission system and explain with the aid of a diagram a method of overcoming the problem.

18 What percentage slip can be expected from a flat belt?

19 State the difference between hydrodynamic and hydrostatic lubrication systems.

20 Why are greases sometimes preferred to oil as a lubricant?

21 What is meant by 'film strength'?

22 Name a solid lubricant contained in grease.

23 What is meant by 'mist lubrication'? How is it achieved?

24 What type of seal would be used in an application where there is relative movement between the parts which need to be sealed?

25 List FIVE safety precautions that must be observed in relation to transmission mechanism.

BACKGROUND TO TECHNOLOGY

SUBJECT MATTER OF SECTIONS 1-8

SECTION 1

Basic Physical Quantities, Electricity and Magnetism

1 Introduction to the SI system
2 Structure and states of matter
3 Mass, force and weight
4 Mass per unit volume
5 Basic theory of electricity
6 Circuits
7 Magnetism

SECTION 2

Forces

1 Effects of force
2 Resultant and equilibrant forces
3 Resolution of forces
4 Moments; the theorem of moments
5 Conditions of equilibrium
6 Centre of gravity; equilibrium and stability
7 Friction

SECTION 3

Pressure

1 Pressure
2 Pressure exerted by liquids
3 Pressure in gases
4 Pressure on liquids
5 Connected vessels
6 Upthrust

SECTION 4

Heat

1 Heat and energy
2 Melting and solidifying
3 Evaporation and condensation
4 Dissolving and solidifying
5 Heat transfer

SECTION 5

Thermal Movement

1 Temperature
2 Thermal movement of solids
3 Thermal movement of liquids
4 Thermal movement of gases
5 The gas laws

SECTION 6

Motion

1 Linear motion at uniform velocity
2 Rotation at uniform speed
3 Direct transmission
4 Indirect transmission
5 Uniform acceleration from rest
6 Uniform acceleration and deceleration

SECTION 7

Energy

1 Force, mass and acceleration
2 Work
3 Power; rating and efficiency of machines
4 Potential and kinetic energy
5 Centripetal and centrifugal force

SECTION 8

Principles of tool construction; materials technology

1 Tools using the lever principle
2 Tools based on the pulley
3 Inclined plane and hydraulic equipment
4 Materials subject to tension and compression
5 Materials subject to shear

Note

All the books of 'Technology of Skilled Processes' are in one way or another related to the series 'Background to Technology'. In the case of 'Power Transmission' the sections 1.1, 1.3, 1.4, 2.1, 2.2, 2.3, 2.4, 2.5, 2.6, 2.7, 3.1, 3.2, 3.3, 3.4, 3.5, 4.1, 4.5, 5.1, 5.2, 5.3, 5.4, 5.5, 6.1, 6.2, 6.3, 6.4, 6.5, 6.6, 7.1, 7.2, 7.3, 7.4, 7.5 and 8.3 must be studied and will be examined.

Information about the Syllabus and the books of Background to Technology can be obtained from
The City and Guilds of London Institute,
76 Portland Place,
London W1N4 AA
or from the Publisher of these books
Stam Press Ltd,
Old Station Drive,
Cheltenham GL53 ODN

GUILDFORD COUNTY COLLEGE
OF TECHNOLOGY LIBRARY
AUTHOR Butterworth N A ed. et al
TITLE Power Transmission
CLASS 621.86 BUT
63581